My Owr

My Own Private Idaho

Gus Van Sant

faber and faber

First published in the United States in 1993 by Faber and Faber, Inc.,
50 Cross Street, Winchester, MA 01890, and the United Kingdom by
Faber and Faber Ltd., 3 Queen Square, London WCIN 3AU.

My Own Private Idaho © 1991 Idaho Productions, Inc.
Introduction © 1993 by Graham Fuller and Gus Van Sant

Stills for *My Own Private Idaho* © Abigayle Tarsches
Portraits of Gus Van Sant and stills from *Mala Noche*
© Eric Alan Edwards
Stills of *Drugstore Cowboy* and *Chimes at Midnight* courtesy of BFI
Stills, Posters and Designs

Special thanks to Judith Verno and her associates at
New Line Cinema

CIP records for this book are available from the British Library
and the Library of Congress

ISBN 0 571 20259 4

Printed and bound in Great Britain by
Mackays of Chatham plc, Chatham, Kent

2 4 6 8 10 9 7 5 3 1

Contents

Gus Van Sant: Swimming Against the Current

The following interview with Gus Van Sant mostly took place at his rented apartment near Castro Street in San Francisco in April 1993. Van Sant had located himself there in order to begin pre-production on *The Mayor of Castro Street*, a film adaptation of Randy Shilts's biography of Harvey Milk, the city supervisor whose 1978 assassination (alongside that of Mayor George Moscone) made him a martyr for gay rights. Shortly after we talked, Van Sant quietly withdrew from the project, unwilling to direct the version of the script that Oliver Stone and his fellow producers wished to make. It is indicative of Van Sant's independent spirit that he should opt out of a movie that would have featured a bigger star (Robin Williams had been mooted as Harvey Milk), demanded a much bigger investment and got a wider distribution (from Warner Bros.) than each of his previous films. It was a decision that echoed Van Sant's taking *My Own Private Idaho* from a major studio, TriStar, to an aggressive indie, New Line, at a time when the integrity of that particularly personal film had also been compromised. But if this singular director has elected at times to drop down (or off) the big-budget scale to protect his interests, on a purely artistic level he has, in less than a decade, moved from minor to major.

Van Sant's emergence coincided with the lionizing of American independent film in the mid-eighties, an event spurred by the liberal arts media's dissatisfaction with commercial movies and the critical successes of directors like Spike Lee and Jim Jarmusch, specifically the latter, whose *Stranger Than Paradise,* winner of the Camera d'Or at Cannes in 1984, set a style for hipster road movies that has been the genre-of-choice for indie filmmakers since. At Cannes two years later, Jarmusch's *Down by Law,* Lee's *She's Gotta Have It,* and Lizzie Borden's *Working Girls* aggrandized the notion of a cohesive American new wave that has latterly been augmented by the arrival of Hal Hartley, Nancy Savoca, Steven Soderbergh, Todd Haynes, Richard Linklater, Allison Anders, Quentin Tarantino, Sadie Benning, and others. In fact, it is, by its very nature, a disparate movement with no single unifying methodology beyond the guerrilla warfare for backing, a non-studio visual aesthetic, and minority or existential themes (hence the preponderance of road movies).

The director of *Mala Noche* (1985), *Drugstore Cowboy* (1989), *My Own Private Idaho* (1991), and *Even Cowgirls Get the Blues* (1993) stands both inside this loose circle of filmmakers and on its perimeter. Based in Portland, Oregon, and therefore distanced from Hollywood and the indie ferment of New York, Van Sant has certainly inhabited the road genre, but he has extended it to a detached, serio-comic celebration – if 'celebration' can admit so much irony – of outsiderdom and alienation that is nonetheless more emotionally wrenching than, say, Jarmusch's deadpan, synchronous beat fantasies or Hartley's droll, deliberate meditations on young lovers thwarted by happenstance and meddlesome parents. Van Sant's heroes are invariably obsessives and seekers doomed to fail (though as critic Donald Lyons has pointed out, in losing they 'somehow win'*). They are gay men stoically suffering the torments of unrequited love, junkies, male hustlers, and, in *Cowgirls*, a woman hitch-hiker – they are riff-raff, society's detritus, who are ennobled not by any indulgent affection for lowlife on behalf of Van Sant, but by the simple fact that he refuses to moralize about them, to condemn or condone them. What Van Sant actually does do is demythologize their rebel status by making us spend quality quotidian time with them; thus in *Drugstore*, the carrot-topped dealer played by Max Perlich talks TV trivia as much as he does drugs; Matt Dillon's narrator/protagonist Bob may be the swashbuckling leader of his gang of drug-raiders, but he's also a boyish golfer with a clumsy backswing. Van Sant makes these outlaws ordinary.

Attempts to deify the director himself as any kind of

---

*'Gus Van Sant', *Film Comment*, September–October 1991, pp. 6–12.

counter-cultural hero come unstuck, despite his hip attributes. (Van Sant, who hopes one day to film Michael Murphy's *Golf in the Kingdom*, is, like Bob, a keen golfer struggling to get his handicap down.) Palpably influenced by William S. Burroughs (*Drugstore*'s proselytizing junkie priest), John Rechy (*City of Night*), Andy Warhol (whose voyeuristic imperatives and laconic detachment he shares), and Antony Balch (who filmed Burroughs shooting up in *Towers Open Fire*), Van Sant is at the vanguard of so-called 'queer' cinema in America. But that's more because directors like Haynes, Benning, and Tom Kalin have yet to achieve his commercial and critical success than because of the polemical vigour of Van Sant's work. Although the Harvey Milk film would have inevitably been activist, Van Sant is essentially a gay director of films rather than a director of gay films (*Drugstore*'s two couples are straight; Cissy Hankshaw's lesbian adventures in *Cowgirls* are not overtly political). In allowing himself to filter the stories he chooses to film through his own taciturn, egalitarian, and wry sensibility rather than being led by a predetermined agenda, Van Sant makes the gay (or junkie, or hitch-hiker) experience more readily communicable to wide audiences than the more self-consciously homoerotic or strident films of some of his contemporaries. Sexual orientation is less of an issue in his work than common emotions like repressed desire or the ache for family and home. Sex itself in Van Sant's films is Warholian: cold, commercial, elliptically framed.

Van Sant has spiralled from the neo-noir expressionism of *Mala Noche* to a loose, jagged, naturalistic style that has incorporated time-lapse photography, home movies, modernized Shakespeare, surrealism (the drug hallucinations in *Drugstore*; the Magritte-like 'face' at the end of the blacktop in *Idaho*), jokey tableaux (*Idaho*'s living, breathing porno magazine display), and ubiquitous playfulness. I make a claim for him as one of the great visual poets of modern cinema, an inheritor of Welles's theatricalism and Pasolini's low-life lyricism — less classical than romantic, though steeped in avant-garde experimentalism. Far more a laureate of the Pacific Northwest than the David Lynch of *Twin Peaks*, Van Sant anticipated the power of insalubriousness as a style before grunge became the region's high-export contribution to nineties rock culture.

He was born in Louisville, Kentucky, in 1952, the son of middle-class parents, Betty and Gus Van Sant Sr., a travelling salesman who became a sportswear and women's clothing company executive. The family moved to Darien, Connecticut, and then to Portland, where Van Sant attended the progressive Catlin Gabel School before enrolling as a film major at the Rhode Island School of Design. In 1976, after spending some time in Europe, he moved to Los Angeles, joining the Paramount-based staff of writer/director Ken Shapiro, who had spun a cult movie from hit TV show *The Groove Tube*. Having directed a short, *The Discipline of DE*, which was shown at the New York Film Festival, Van Sant was encouraged by Shapiro to circumvent the Hollywood machinery and raise independent money for his own projects, and in 1981, supported by his father, he directed his first feature, *Alice in Hollywood*. A screwball comedy about a would-be Hollywood starlet who does time on Sunset Boulevard before she makes it on TV, it was neither completed nor released and, disappointed, Van Sant returned to the East Coast. He worked in a warehouse and then with a Manhattan ad agency, writing scripts in his spare time. The money he saved enabled him to finance *Mala Noche*, based on a novella by Walt Curtis, an underground poet in Portland, which Van Sant turned into his own city of night, shooting the movie in shimmering black and white, replete with looming close-ups and haunting expressionistic angles. With the pathetic-comic saga of Walt (Tim Streeter), a convenience store manager who's forlornly in love with a Mexican teenager, the movie set a tone of cool despair and implied sado-masochism: like Bob in *Drugstore* and Mike (River Phoenix), the narcoleptic street boy in *Idaho*, Walt is anguished beneath his sexy, insouciant demeanour; like Bob and Mike, he loves someone who is destined to leave him; like them, he is last seen travelling to a new adventure or some kind of oblivion. Sissy Hankshaw, the pregnant 'progenitor of a tribe' at the end of *Cowgirls*, is the first Van Sant protagonist to find serenity and promise continuity.

Van Sant is still to make a studio film—*Drugstore* was produced by the now defunct Avenue Pictures and *Idaho* and *Cowgirls* by New Line—although he is likely to direct Buck Henry's screen adaptation of *To Die For* for Columbia as his next project. He himself has assured continuity as an American *auteur* if he can preserve his own corner of the field, his own private Idaho, although serenity is unlikely to become one of the watchwords of his oeuvre—we look to him to unnerve us more than we do to comfort us. That unsettling process, however, is never gratuitous or cheap (nor yet Lynchian). If Van Sant corroborates our sense that life *is* unsettling, marked by yearnings rather than by the cosy affirmations that Hollywood habitually offers, his resilient humour protects both us and his protagonists from maudlin responses. Melodic in their realism, unflinching in their acceptance of death, and anti-sentimental, Van Sant's films are as sure, as adult, and as commanding as those of Howard Hawks—*Drugstore Cowboy* as jaunty in its eulogizing of professionalism as *Only Angels Have Wings, Even Cowgirls Get the Blues* a perverse feminist analogue to *Red River*. There is, of course, no higher accolade.

Graham Fuller
June 1993

GRAHAM FULLER: *What are your earliest memories of needing to express yourself in an artistic way, through painting or writing?*

GUS VAN SANT: When I was about twelve or thirteen, I had this teacher—Bob Levine, his name was—in junior high school, and there was a whole group of students who religiously took his art class. We all *had* to take the class, but a bunch of us worked after school because we were entertained by him and he encouraged people. He, I think, was my inspiration in the early days. I actually remember him creating paintings in class, and then, on my own, I would emulate his style of painting, which was sort of the New York advertising world illustration style, design- or magazine-oriented as opposed to fine art. There was another, famous Robert Levine who did illustrations—I remember him doing one for Aqueduct Raceway—whose style was actually quite a bit like my teacher Robert Levine's style. It was the kind of stuff that was similar to what Warhol did in the fifties, except that it was in the sixties. I remember it being acrylic mixed in with tissue paper and then paint and gold leaf. I think of it as this kind of Greenwich Village, gay thing, because my teacher was an out gay teacher in 1963, which was pretty unusual for this very WASPy area where I lived in Darien, Connecticut. So, he was an early influence. Also we were doing a lot of silkscreening, just as Warhol was at that time, unbeknownst to me because I didn't know who Warhol was. We silkscreened posters and occasionally we would do artistic, multilayered silkscreens that were more like works of art.

Then there was our English teacher, David Sohn, who encouraged us to make films. He was a progressive writing teacher who had written this book called *Stop, Look and Write*. It was a book of photographs, and the point was to look at a photograph and then write about what might be happening in it. It was kind of McLuhan-esque, and I think David even recommended McLuhan in his class—pretty unusual reading for fourteen-year-olds. He also showed us *Citizen Kane* and Canadian Film

Board films that were definitely influenced by McLuhan, because they were an abstract barrage of voices and media images that didn't necessarily make sense. I remember writing a visual piece in David's class—like an illustrated novel, but short, ten pages or so. I still have that.

GF: *You also made some animated shorts with your parents' home-movie camera.*

GVS: We'd emulate guys like Norman McClaren and Robert Breer in our spare time and then show the films in class; although I don't remember ever showing a film myself. We'd come to Robert Levine and explain things that we'd seen over in David's class and I remember the art teacher being jealous of the English teacher. He claimed that they were art films and they weren't appropriate for the English class! Anyway, between the two of them, I was influenced a lot.

GF: *Do those teachers know your films?*

GVS: Oh, I'm sure. Bob Levine came to the opening of *My Own Private Idaho* at the New York Film Festival.

GF: *At what stage did you make* The Happy Organ?

GVS: During one summer I worked in my dad's company's mailroom on Fifth Avenue in New York and I spent the money that I made on a really developed Super-8 camera. I made films with that for a couple of years and then we moved to Oregon. Eric Edwards and I, who were friends in high school, decided to make *The Happy Organ* for our senior project; Eric later shot *My Own Private Idaho* and *Even Cowgirls Get the Blues* with John Campbell. Originally, the school project was just going to be in 8mm, but we decided to make it in 16 with sound. It was about twenty minutes long, black and white.

GF: *It was about a brother and sister who go on a weekend trip and the sister gets killed on the road. Where did that come from?*

GVS: I don't know. I just made it up. Fiction.

GF: *After that, in 1970, you went to the Rhode Island School of Design but you more or less gave up painting there. Why was that?*

GVS: Well, I painted at RISD, but I majored in film. Most of the kids there were painters or photographers or architects. Most people were interested in film, and maybe some of them went into filmmaking like I did, but nobody that I knew went to the school specifically for film, because the department was pretty small; it was known as an art school, though there were jewellery-makers and fashion students there, too. I remember a lot of students were very eager to get out of painting because there was apparently no future in it. Not too many students who had graduated with painting degrees had really gotten anywhere with their paintings.

GF: *David Byrne was there at that time, wasn't he?*

GVS: And the rest of the Talking Heads. Chris Frantz was taking one of the video courses and I remember he got his friends – David was one of them – to mime 'Mustang Sally' to a record, and they pretended they were a rock band on video. That was the first thing that I ever saw the Talking Heads do. I don't know if it was a statement, but it was like a funky art video. They wore wigs and fooled around.

GF: *Was there something in the air at RISD at the time?*

GVS: Yeah, the Providence Aesthetic, as Mary Clark used to call it. Mary Clark was a member of the Motels, which came out of sixties rock 'n' roll and drug influences. There was a bunch of art bands that were influenced by Martin Mull, who was a painter at RISD in the sixties and had a band called Soup. He was kind of the grandfather of my generation, though I didn't know him. A guy named Tim Duffy had a band called Snake and the Snatch and there were other bands like Iron Grandmother and Electric Driveway; they all had the same lineup, but they would change their costumes and come out and play as different bands from different eras. They were comedy-oriented, multimedia bands – 'painter bands' I would call them because none of the people in them were musicians, although they put together these shows which had very funny lyrics and a lot of pageantry and costume changes. Some people did performance pieces on stage, like one girl sat under a sun lamp for fifteen minutes between sets. Frank Zappa and the Mothers of Invention were probably an inspiration for all these people and I think everybody was influenced by the Velvet Underground at the time — because they were a painter band — and by the Warhol scene.

Nearly everybody stayed in Providence and most of them still live there and work as bartenders or teachers or whatever. But the Talking Heads — David, Chris, and Tina [Weymouth] — went to New York and forced themselves to stay there and pursued *serious* music as opposed to the Providence Style, which was not serious!

Meanwhile, I had left for LA. But that whole scene had had a real strong effect on me. There were two guys, Charlie Clavery and Scott Sorensen, who had a video project called *Meet the Stars*. If someone famous came to town, they would try to get in the backstage door without credentials, and see how far they could get — and that was the video! Charlie would act like a newscaster, except he'd wear a wig or funny glasses, and he would try and get an unauthorized interview and sometimes he would succeed. To this day I'm influenced by them and by the Motels and the multimedia approach and the humour within their projects. You don't really see a direct kind of influence in my work; it's just that they were inspirational. Some day I'd like to make a film about them.

GF: *What films were you seeing at this time?*

GVS: I was mostly influenced by the sixties experimental filmmakers who were also painters, like Stan Brakhage, Warhol, Ron Rice, Taylor Mead, Jordan Belson, who is a San Francisco painter; a lot of the San Francisco Canyon Cinema co-op people and the New York Anthology Film Archives people like Jonas Mekas. I don't think that I was directly influenced by anyone else, except to try and emulate commercial filmmakers and assimilate drama into my films once I had left RISD. The very last film I made there, my senior project, had an experimental tack, but it tried to incorporate a slick Hollywood format, like the Godard films. Although I didn't know much about Godard, and I still don't, I've realized that that was something he was doing. His films tended to look like

xv

Hollywood films, but their stories and techniques were messed with and mixed up. I did something like that in a film called *Late Morning Start*. It was a failure, really, but it looked good and it was interesting. Its intention was to draw you into all these different stories, but not show you what happened; your attention was continually diverted. Bunuel's *Le Fantôme de la Liberté* did exactly the same thing, but I did it less successfully because I didn't have the budget.

GF: *When you moved to Los Angeles in 1976, you worked for a couple of years as a production assistant for writer-director Ken Shapiro. Tell me about that experience.*

GVS: Shapiro was working at Paramount. He had started *Channel One*, which was really the origins of *Saturday Night Live*-type skit humour. It was like hippie performance theatre and *The Village Voice* dubbed it *The Groove Tube*. They were also working with video and made a lot of fake commercials for things like drugs.

Ken took *The Groove Tube* on the college circuit and realized that there was a big market for this kind of thing. So he used his own money that he had saved up from being a child star in the fifties – he had appeared on *The Milton Berle Show* – and recreated *The Groove Tube* on 35mm film. It was a pretty slick production. The reason I started working for him was that Chevy Chase had done this interview in a *Los Angeles Times* Sunday supplement, and he said he was going to visit his old friend, Ken Shapiro – this was around February '76. So I looked Ken up in the phone book and called him, and he put me to work as his assistant because all his friends had left to do *Saturday Night Live*. At the time, Lorne Michaels was working for Ken as a writer, and they were writing this thing called *Ma Bell*, which was about Joey Schneider's rip-off of the phone company – an 18-year-old guy tampering with the phone system. It was about Phone Phreaks and it was a pretty exciting project. Ken was a very counter-cultural sort of person who smoked joints during the day as he wrote, scheming on his next film project for Paramount. At the time, it seemed like the kids were taking over the studios. As Ken's assistant, I thought it was going to be Easy Street for me from then on, which wasn't true. He did make a film called *Modern Problems*, but he became very negative about the studio system.

GF: *Why didn't you stay in Hollywood?*

GVS: I was being paid by Paramount through Ken, and when his contract ran out, he didn't hire me any longer. During the shooting of *Modern Problems*, I was the odd man out, because his wife got the job as his assistant, and there were too many producers involved for him to get all his friends jobs. So I didn't get to work on that one.

GF: *Around that time you directed a film called* Alice in Hollywood. *What became of it?*

GVS: It exists. I never sold it. I should probably try and sell it now.

GF: *You could probably find an audience for it now.*

GVS: Maybe. At the time I couldn't. When I finished it, I tried entering it into the LA Film Festival and the Atlanta Film Festival, but they wouldn't take it. So I felt like it didn't have a market at all. It was supposed to be a feature-length film, and I didn't think it really held up at an hour and a half, so I cut it down to forty-five minutes. It was a kind of ridiculous comedy, which is a dangerous area to work in. Even the big-budget films that attempt the ridiculous comedy genre fail. I was trying something too difficult, although I didn't know it at the time. I never got my money back from that.

GF: *Did it have any of the ideas that you've explored since?*

GVS: Yeah, some of them are quite similar because I wrote the script. But other little films that I made had a more serious edge; it didn't have that.

GF: *It's about a girl who comes to Hollywood and ends up living on the street, right?*

GVS: She ends up living in a car and eventually achieves notoriety as a television actress. Then she leaves her street friends behind because she's found a different strata of people. I think it was a comment on Hollywood friendships; the way I guess I'd learned to know them.

How people climb up a certain ladder and have business relationships instead of personal ones. It had that side to it, but it wasn't really stressed. The other side was this absurd comedy that was supposed to be a take-off of *Alice in Wonderland.*

GF: *You wrote several scripts around this time, including* The Corporate Vampire *and* Mister Popular. *What can you tell me about those?*

GVS: They exist as scripts. I wrote *Corporate Vampire* in New York. It was about a corporation that had a very exclusive higher echelon of presidents and vice presidents that were all vampires and a man who is promoted and initiated into their group. It's a *Rosemary's Baby* kind of thing. *Mister Popular,* originally called *The Projectionist,* was a story about a high school kid who influences his fellow students by subliminally introducing advertising images through audio-visual techniques. He gets the student body under his control and becomes the most popular kid in the school. I wrote it while I was living in Hollywood as the next project that I was going to do after *Alice.*

GF: *When you came to live in New York in 1983 you worked in an ad agency. Did you direct commercials?*

GVS: No, I was a junior producer. I did the technical work of booking mixing stages, that sort of thing. It wasn't really that important, what I was doing. I organized the company's slide show and stuff like that.

GF: *But you were able to save up enough money to make* Mala Noche.

GVS: Right.

GF: *What was it about Walt Curtis's novel that appealed to you? Why did you want to turn it into a film?*

GVS: In 1977 I had gone up to Portland to work on this film, *Property,* directed by Penny Allen, who had gotten a CETA grant for about $80,000. I was the sound man and Eric Edwards was the cinematographer. One of the lead actors was Walt Curtis, who was a Portland poet. He had, along with Mississippi Mud, a non-profit organization, printed this book called *Mala Noche.* And I remembered it as being really strong. It was Walt's first semi-novel; it was like a journal, in a way, one of the few prose things that he had written. I was writing a few things at the time but I thought *Mala Noche* was better than anything I was writing, and I knew that Walt would probably let me film his novella. Also, I could go back to Portland, which is where I wanted to live. There was a small film community there with one or two cameras floating around and some aspiring filmmakers who I could probably get to help me out. So I moved there to make the movie.

I thought *Mala Noche* was the kind of story that Hollywood wouldn't ever make and it was my new philosophy that my next project *should* be something they wouldn't ever make. That way you could keep it pure, simply in terms of the subject matter.

GF: *Were you consciously setting out to tell a story of unrequited gay love, or was it just unrequited love?*

GVS: No, it was unrequited gay love for sure. But I thought that if it was a good movie, it would relate to anybody— not solely to a gay audience. I had seen some gay films in Hollywood before I had left and had been to a gay film festival in New York. I witnessed how basic the films were at those festivals, and how there was a large audience that came to see them but there wasn't really any product, not even in low-budget films. *Taxi Zum Klo* came out before I made *Mala Noche*, and I think it was really the first independent film about gay life that did well in the regular marketplace. It became quite a big hit in certain cities around the United States, even in Portland, attracting straight as well as gay audiences. I remember that being a cue that I could maybe film Walt's story and get my money back. When you're making a film you always wonder whether or not it will break even.

GF: Mala Noche *coincided with* My Beautiful Laundrette *in 1985. Both films were significant in the way that they presented love between men without turning it into a polemical issue or a forbidden fruit.*

GVS: *Mala Noche* didn't really get shown that year, but it was at the Berlin Film Festival at the same time. I remember there was this Australian guy who I hoped would buy

Mala Noche, but he spent all his money on *My Beautiful Laundrette*. *Mala Noche* played at gay festivals for a few years, but nothing really happened to it until *Drugstore Cowboy* came out. It finally broke even this year. It only cost $25,000 and it's taken almost ten years to make its money back.

GF: *At times the cinematography of* Mala Noche *reminds me of* Touch of Evil. *You used a lot of huge close-ups in it, a very tightly packed frame, and some very weird expressionistic angles. How did you arrive at that style?*

GVS: It was probably a combination of things. It was black and white and Orson Welles's cinematography and David Lynch's *Eraserhead* were very influential. David Lynch had a certain lighting style – pretty minimal, but also very expressionistic – which I adopted when we were lighting interiors. He used spotlights and so I got a bunch of spotlights. Stanley Kubrick's black and white films were another influence.

GF: *The sequence in* Mala Noche *where you first see the home movie is surprising because it's in colour. You used home movies again in* Drugstore Cowboy *and* My Own Private Idaho.

GVS: *Paris, Texas* used home movies and I think I had seen it just before I began *Mala Noche*. There was a passage in *Mala Noche*, the novel, where the boys take photographs, but I had them making movies instead; it worked much better.

GF: *Pepper, in that macho Chicano way, doesn't want to acknowledge that he's having sex with a man. In a similar sense, nor does Scott in* My Own Private Idaho *fully embrace it. And, in fact, isn't Pepper in some ways the blueprint for Scott in an early version of the script you wrote for* Idaho?

GVS: I guess they're similar characters. I think the origins of *Mala Noche* and *My Own Private Idaho* were John Rechy's novel *City of Night*, which had characters who admitted to being street hustlers but not to being gay – there was something about taking money for sex that validated that. After Pepper spent the night with Walt [played by Tim

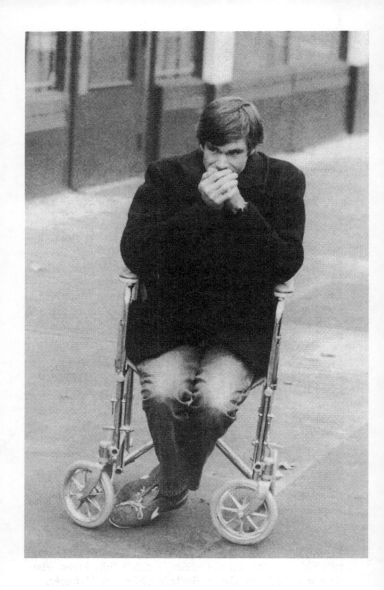

Streeter], he stole ten dollars. Certainly there was this whole machismo kind of thing going on, since he was from Mexico.

In Scott's case, in *My Own Private Idaho*, I was fashioning those characters after people that I had met in Portland who are street hustlers; the same things that were in the characters in John Rechy's book existed within them. I wanted to expose that side. I don't know if it came out of *Mala Noche*. I think it came out of the paradox of people having sex with someone of the same sex yet refusing the label that this gave them.

GF: *Isn't there a direct link between Pepper and Scott? You'd written a short story about the actor, Ray Monge, who played Pepper, and his cousin Little George, which became part of the* Idaho *script.*

GVS: Well, in fashioning *My Own Private Idaho,* there were a number of scripts that I was writing. The original script was written in the seventies when I was living in Hollywood. It was actually set on Hollywood Boulevard, but when I read *City of Night,* which was also set there, I realized that that was so much better than what I was writing. I stopped writing, and decided that either I'd do *City of Night* or else I shouldn't do this project.

Meanwhile, I had shot *Mala Noche* and eight years went by. Then I started writing again about these same street characters. Actually, when I was editing *Mala Noche,* I had met Mike, who became the sort of guide to the character of Mike in the film.

GF: *Was he a narcoleptic?*

GVS: No. But he smoked a lot of pot, and as a sort of defense mechanism, he would say he had forgotten something. You know, if you said, 'Why weren't you here when you said you'd be here?' or whatever, he'd say, 'Well, I don't remember that.' So it seemed like he had narcolepsy.

So I was writing this thing about Mike, who had a friend named Scott. In the script, I made him a rich kid, although he wasn't in reality. Although I think there were rich kids like that on the streets, I didn't fully know who he was until I saw Orson Welles's *Chimes at Midnight.*

Seeing that, I realized that Shakespeare's *Henry IV* plays had this gritty quality about them. They had the young Henry, Prince Hal, who is about to become king, slumming on the streets with his sidekick. The young Henry seemed to be Scott and the sidekick seemed to be Mike, so I adapted the Shakespeare story to modern Portland. It was called *In a Blue Funk* or *Minions of the Moon*; it had a lot of different titles. At that time I had, through *Mala Noche*, gotten an agent, and I showed the script to somebody at 20th Century-Fox who liked Shakespeare. Eventually we toned the Shakespeare down and made the language more modern. But at the time it was literally, from beginning to end, a restructuring of the *Henry IV* plays.

I was also working on this short story called *My Own Private Idaho* which I intended to film. It was about twenty-five pages long and about Ray and Little George. Ray was the guy who played Pepper in *Mala Noche* and Little George was his cousin. They were real people, but the characters that I was writing were like Mike and Scott. They were two Latino characters on the streets of Portland. Ray was eighteen, a street hustler, and Little George was a thirteen-year-old homeless kid with a dog. They went on the road in search of their parents, or some relative, and to a town in Spain that had the same last name as Ray's character. I don't think I had a town name in my story; I was trying to figure out what that was going to be. Ray was going to randomly look up somebody with his last name and assume that he was related, and the people in the town were going to think that they were American relatives. Then they were going to live in Spain until Ray fell in love with a girl and went off on honeymoon, leaving Little George behind with this dog. That's where that part of Scott and Mike's story came from in the film.

Then I had another script called *The Boys of Storytown*, or something like that, which had the Mike and Scott characters. That was the part of the story where they were on the street. In that, Mike has narcolepsy and keeps passing out, Scott has just come to town and runs into this German guy, Hans, who Mike had lived with for a while. In the movie he doesn't, but in one of these early scripts, he lived with Hans for half the film and they had this funny domestic relationship. Then he leaves Hans and goes back on the street, and there's a character named Bob . . . I don't remember what happened after that. It could have just been a half-written thing.

I wanted to make this film but it didn't really have a cohesive script. When *Drugstore Cowboy* happened, it took up my time for about a year and a half, after which I decided that I would refine *My Own Private Idaho* by combining these three scripts together, which I did while we were editing *Drugstore*. It combined the Ray–George characters with the Mike–Scott characters, and I threw the Shakespeare in the middle and bookended it with the other stories. I mixed it all together and used that as my structure. Finally, I hammered out the version which became *My Own Private Idaho*. By the time *Drugstore Cowboy* came out, it was finished and I declared it as my next project and that it was going to star the original Mike and that I had somebody, Rodney, who was going to play Scott.

You know, it's all kind of mixed up! Ray, in the story, was never really *Ray*, and Scott didn't necessarily come from Ray in *Mala Noche*. Everything was influencing everything else. I think that the tentatively non-gay hustler character is to be found in many places.

GF: *You seem to blur the notions of sexual identity purposely, as if labels like 'gay' and 'straight' aren't particularly helpful. Again, in* Even Cowgirls Get the Blues, *Sissy Hankshaw has sex with both men and women, but her sexual identity isn't really the issue.*

GVS: Well, I don't know. I guess all these stories are concerned with showing that. Walt in *Mala Noche* is always talking about it, asking, What does it mean? And then Sissy in Tom Robbins's novel is this pan-sexual character who finds delight in the sexuality of women, and that is presented as an OK thing. The characters in *My Own*

Private Idaho are literally blurred because their sexuality is a business as opposed to an emotion. They occupy a different space, I think, than Walt and Pepper and Sissy Hankshaw.

Those were just the projects that I was picking up at the time. I guess it reflects my own point of view, maybe artistically rather than politically.

GF: *Where did you come across James Fogle's unpublished novel* Drugstore Cowboy?

GVS: Through the Portland group of filmmakers, I had met Daniel Yost, whose brother Jack Yost had helped Penny Allen raise $125,000 for *Paydirt*, which was the film she made after *Property*. When I moved to Portland, I thought I could use a producer, and I asked Jack if he would raise the money for *Mala Noche*. He was half interested, but he was also cautious because he thought that Walt's novel wouldn't make such a good film. Dan Yost, a sportswriter who had become associated with the film consortium, had worked with Thomas E. Gaddis, who had written the book *The Birdman of Alcatraz*. In one of his classes, Gaddis had told Dan about James Fogle, who was a novelist in prison who couldn't really get his manuscripts around. By the time I showed up, these manuscripts had been sitting in Dan's cabinet for about seven or eight years and he had tried writing a screenplay from one of them, *Satan's Sandbox*. I actually liked that one better than *Drugstore Cowboy*. It was a prison triangle involving an effeminate black transvestite, Ivy, who ran a beauty parlour in prison, and two other inmates, Mike, unbelievably enough, and Ivy's former lover, Zitzer, who was a real guy. This was in San Quentin, where Fogle had spent time. Mike, who was about eighteen and had been thrown into prison for causing a traffic accident where two women were killed, falls in love with Ivy and they have this torrid semi-gay love affair, to the amusement of Zitzer. It was a comment on sexuality in prison, which has different rules from sexuality outside of prison.

I think Dan had originally shown it to me because it

made a connection with *Mala Noche*. Since I'd been out in Hollywood pitching *My Own Private Idaho*, he felt that I could pitch Fogle's manuscripts. So I started pitching them and then it became obvious that we needed to fashion scripts of them on spec.

GF: *Did you just write* Drugstore?

GVS: Both of them. Then eventually Avenue Pictures decided to produce *Drugstore Cowboy*.

GF: *Where does your affinity for street kids and junkies and hustlers come from and why do you seek to tell their stories? Is that in any way a reaction to your own middle-class upbringing?*

GVS: It's certainly very much apart from my own upbringing. I think it's that *Mala Noche, Drugstore Cowboy,* and *My Own Private Idaho* had settings that were unfamiliar enough to me that they seemed like fairytale land. Perhaps a need to tell a certain type of story that was set in a place that I didn't know anything about; adventure could be had because it's a land far away. In the case of *Mala Noche*, it was a land of transients and loggers and winos in a grocery on Skid Row. In *Drugstore Cowboy*, it was a land of holdup men and drug addicts. Then in *Idaho*, it was a land of homeless kids who sold themselves for money on the streets. All three of them are close to each other, but far away from the public, from the viewers, in the sense that *Star Wars* or pirate adventures are far away from them. It's a storyteller's technique to remove you from everyday life into a new area, so parables can be had.

GF: *The difference is that you are dealing with worlds that do exist and which are very harsh.*

GVS: So are space adventures and pirate adventures—probably more harsh.

GF: *In* Drugstore Cowboy, *you didn't attempt to romanticize the junkies or to judge them. The film came out right at the time of Nancy Reagan's 'Just Say No' campaign, but you removed yourself from that—and from IV-transmitted AIDS—by setting the film in the early seventies. You have*

described Drugstore Cowboy *as an anti-drug film. What's your take on it now?*

GVS: I think it was an anti-drug film, except it came from a book by a drug user as opposed to a drug non-user. That gave it a stronger voice in terms of the anti-drugs position, because a user knows what he's speaking about. One of the strengths of the film is that it's coming from the voice of somebody who lived that life. Ever since Fogle started dealing with drugs—he's in his fifties now—I think he's been caught in a trap that he can't get out of. Largely because of the film, I think, he was able to get out of prison but, over a year ago, he was arrested in a motel not unlike the one that's in the movie, in possession of a lot of drugs. As long as he was out of prison, he was in this other kind of prison. The whole experience is Pavlovian—he describes it as such in the book of *Drugstore Cowboy* and we show it in the movie. It's an insider's view as opposed to an outsider's view.

GF: *Clearly you didn't want the film to be preachy.*

GVS: I didn't think we needed to be. I didn't feel that we had to be obvious. All the things that the movie says, the book says, are said in the same way: 'Make up your own mind.'

I think that the movie can be hard for somebody who's just quit drugs. I don't think it helps them very much to watch *Drugstore Cowboy*. But then again, if they've just quit, they probably shouldn't go see a movie about drugs anyway. It's different for a person that quit a long time ago, while a person who's never used drugs can see from the film that it's not too much fun. So it can work as an anti-drug film.

GF: *William S. Burroughs plays* Drugstore Cowboy's *junkie priest and patron saint. You've also directed Burrough's* The Disciple of D.E. *and a film of him reading his poem 'Thanksgiving Prayer' against the backdrop of the American flag. Can you tell me a little bit about your fascination with Burroughs? I believe you began corresponding with him nearly twenty years ago.*

GVS: I was always interested in his style and his theories. I met him in 1975. I'd read *Naked Lunch*, which was a popular

college book in the sixties, and by 1975 he had written *The Ticket That Exploded* and *The Wild Boys* and I read those. *The Discipline of D.E.*, which was published in a collection of stories called *Exterminator*, wasn't really like any of his other stories. It wasn't as outrageous. It was a pretty matter-of-fact parody about discipline, about the art of self-control, but it was useful, too. It was really the first film that I made out of college, before *Alice In Hollywood*. I used the money that I had made doing sound on *Property* to make it. My parents lived in Connecticut and I was visiting New York City one Christmas and I found William's number in the phone book, so I just called him up and told him I wanted permission to direct a film based on his story, though I didn't have any money to option it. He said it sounded like a good project, so I asked him if I could come visit and he said I could after the holidays and I went into the city and met him. Things were really happening for him then because it was the beginning of the New York punk movement and he was reading his stuff in punk clubs and becoming associated with Patti Smith and others.

He said it would be OK for me to use his story, so I contacted his agent and made the film. It has made a little bit of money. William knew it wouldn't make much because he had made some short films himself with Antony Balch. Ten years later I worked on some records that used William's words and I contacted him again then; he was by then a much more public figure. Two or three years after that, when we were casting *Drugstore Cowboy*, I thought maybe he would be interested in playing Tom the Priest – and he was.

GF: *Did he write his own lines for* Drugstore Cowboy?

GVS: Yeah, James Graverholz and William wrote some things. They had some things that they wanted to do with Tom, and I allowed them to do that, to change the character a little bit.

GF: *In a technical sense, how did you achieve the hallucinogenic effects, the little filigree shapes that float in front of Bob's eyes when he's tripping?*

GVS: They were just little models that we rented or bought. We made them spin and shot them against a white wall and then double-exposed them like they would have done in the thirties. It was pretty simple. We didn't have very much money for special effects, so we did them on our own. One word for those scenes would be expositionary.

GF: *When you do shots like the magnified close-up of the printing on the light bulb in* Drugstore Cowboy *is that stuff that happens extemporaneously?*

GVS: No, I had done that sort of thing in *Mala Noche* and I was hoping to do it again in *Drugstore Cowboy*. We never had time during shooting so we did them while we were editing. We chose specific places in the film where those close-ups would appear and then we got props and actually shot them in the editing room. That light bulb was from the editing table lamp!

GF: *I don't know how you interpret that stuff, or if you even care to interpret it. To me it's like punctuation.*

GVS: A lot of people think it works well in the film because a drug addict might focus on something that small, a light bulb or a match or something like that, and just stare at it, which is true, actually. Maybe we were cueing off a sort of aesthetic that was working its way into the script from the book. It was a stylistic device that I'd been playing with since I started photographing objects in the sixties. I remember buying bellows for my camera so that I could shoot things extremely close up. In my high school year book in Portland there're two pages of photographs of things that are so close you can't really tell what they are. There are things in my other films that relate to visual motifs that I've used. For example, the barn crashing into the road in *Idaho* was a motif that I had painted pictures of for about ten years. Those things are just a way to shoot something that works well and which is an essential part of my style.

GF: *Do you allow yourself to improvise visually, to depart from the script when you're shooting, or is everything very carefully mapped out?*

GVS: We improvise things. Each film has a way of achieving

its own style, a path. *Mala Noche* was storyboarded and we stuck to the storyboards; I figured out what we were doing before we shot it. *Drugstore Cowboy* was much more of an ordeal because of the way it was shot and the size of the crew. Improvisation happened a lot more in that simply because I wasn't able to stick to my storyboards; I was only able to pick up things as we went. And then *Idaho* was not storyboarded at all. It was also shot without any shot list. On *Drugstore Cowboy* I had a shot list and I'd rehearse the scene and then decide in what order I was going to shoot what. On *Idaho* we *didn't* decide in what order we were going to shoot. We always shot the 'first' thing, whatever I decided it should be, and then I'd choose the second shot. We'd usually start wide and then go closer, because it's easier to light that way. Then the same thing happened on *Cowgirls*. We'd just sort of shoot the first shot first, and then because each scene tended to have its own logic, we'd know what to do next.

GF: *What about dialogue—do you allow actors to improvise or experiment with that?*

GVS: Yeah, they do a lot.

GF: *Do you rehearse each scene as it comes up, or do you rehearse the whole film first?*

GVS: I usually have a rehearsal period where we read through the script and do some scenes. But things are locked down when we actually shoot them, so it doesn't help to get too specific before that. Generally we rehearse on the set.

GF: *The best-known example is the fireside scene in Idaho, which was pretty much improvised by River Phoenix and Keanu Reeves.*

GVS: Yeah, they did that themselves. It was a short, three-page scene that River turned into more like an eight-page scene. He added a lot of things and changed the fabric of his character in that scene. He's a songwriter and he worked on it like he does one of his songs, which is very furiously. He had decided that that scene was his character's main scene and, with Keanu's permission, he wrote it out to say something that it wasn't already saying—that his character, Mike, has a crush on Scott and is unable to express it—which wasn't in the script at all. It was his explanation of his character.

GF: *How did you position yourself in order to get* My Own Private Idaho *made?*

GVS: I had basically finished the *Idaho* script eight months before *Drugstore* came out, but I hadn't had many meetings about it. When *Drugstore* started to get press, people in the industry started to talk about it in the same way they started talking about *Reservoir Dogs* last year. So I was this hot new filmmaker amongst this group of hot new filmmakers trying to get attention from the people who back films. Every time I met them, I told them I was going to do *My Own Private Idaho* and that it would only cost a million dollars. They would be very supportive and would want to read it, but after they read it they didn't really want to finance it.

GF: *Was that because of the gay content?*

GVS: It wasn't just the gay content; it was a lot of things. It was partly the way the script was written, which originally had lots of different-sized lettering, unlike a normal script. It was also short—about eighty pages—and the Shakespeare threw them. Basically everything. I think the very first sentence says Mike is getting a blow-job in a motel room. Then he's out on the road and he passes out, and the script talks about the house crashing into the road. It was very disjointed for the readers in Hollywood.

I was also pitching *Cowgirls* at the time and I had my first meeting with Mike Medavoy at Orion. He said it was interesting and about a year later, when he was with TriStar, he decided that I should get the script going. I eventually started working on it when we were editing *Idaho*.

Eventually, I got an offer of $2 million from an outside investor—we thought we had the money, although we didn't actually have it quite yet. At that time, Bruce Weber took a picture of me and the original Mike at the Shangri La in Santa Monica for *Interview* magazine. It was like a publicity stunt. I had bussed Mike down from Portland specifically for the picture, thinking Bruce would probably like the way he looked. So there's this picture of the two of us in front of this mirror, and Mike's hair is wet and he has no shirt on, and it says that he is going to star in *My Own Private Idaho*.

Right about then there was a mix-up between River Phoenix's agent and my producer, Laurie Parker, as to exactly what *My Own Private Idaho* was going to be, because there was another script, called *Revolver*, that somebody was offering River with my name attached. The agent didn't know why the producer of *My Own Private Idaho* didn't know about *Revolver*. She assumed that *My Own Private Idaho* was some sort of trick and she wouldn't let us speak to River. But somehow we found him and I talked to him about the project. Then I had a meeting with Keanu Reeves, who said he was looking for a low-budget film. I told him that it would be done up in Portland and that it would be a small thing, and he thought it was cool. I then went and spent half a day with River in Florida because he was having a hard time making up his mind. Suddenly there was this buzz about the film because all the producers in Hollywood who were trying to cast River and Keanu in their movies were getting the word that they were going to be in *My Own Private Idaho* and they wouldn't have the time to be in the other movies. All these people were coming up to me and congratulating me, even though River and Keanu hadn't committed yet. Finally, they did and that knocked the original choices, Mike and Rodney, into second-string. They were still in the film, but as different characters. We couldn't turn down the opportunity to work with these bigger names. Even then we put it off for nine months or so while River did *Dogfight*. By then, the guy with the money had disappeared, but Laurie shopped it around and got New Line involved. It was quite a saga.

GF: *Had you had to downscale the budget?*

GVS: Oh, no, it was bigger because the actors made it bigger. It was about $2.5 million.

GF: *The* Idaho *script that's published in this book is different in places from the film.*

GVS: It doesn't have the fireside scene that River reworked as it
exists in the film. It's printed the way that it was
originally written so you can see the difference. I don't see
any point in just transcribing the film. The same with
Cowgirls. In both cases the script we worked from was the
one that's being published. It's valuable to be able to see
how things changed during shooting. In *Cowgirls*, there're
whole scenes that appear at the end of the script that are
now at the beginning of the movie. There are scenes in
the script that we shot, but didn't make it into the
finished film.

GF: *When you wrote the* Henry IV *scenes for* Idaho, *did you
actually go back to the text of the plays or was your reference
point* Chimes at Midnight?

GVS: I tried to forget the Welles film because I didn't want to
be plagiaristic or stylistically influenced by it, even though
it had given me the idea. So I referred to the original
Shakespeare. When *My Own Private Idaho* was shown at
the Venice Biennale someone put together a comparative
study of the Shakespeare scenes that I'd used and the
same scenes from a different text of the play. I started to

realize that there were many different versions of Shakespeare.

GF: *Kenneth Branagh's* Henry V *also imported the Falstaff scenes from* Henry IV, Part I.

GVS: Yes, the flashbacks—we used some of the same scenes actually.

GF: *Why did you cut down on the scenes with Jane Lightwork—your version of Mistress Quickly—in the film?*

GVS: There were a couple of different characters that got slimmed down because the Shakespeare scenes were becoming like a movie within the movie. It was interesting up to a point, but in the editing room we were still trying to figure out whether or not it would fly. There was a whole contingent of people at New Line—the domestic distributors—who were totally against the Shakespeare scenes and wanted us to cut them all out. The foreign distributors wanted as much Shakespeare in there as we could get. In the end, we cut out one long scene between Scott and Bob [William Reichert], who are Prince Hal and Falstaff, when they put on a play and Falstaff does this mock-deposing of the king. It was nice, but it went on too long.

GF: *I'm curious to know if you've been influenced by Derek Jarman's Shakespeare films.*

GVS: No. But I was influenced by *The Last of England*, which is Super-8 transferred to video, then manipulated on video and converted back to 35mm; I did the same thing in *The Discipline of D.E.* I liked the way Derek cut *The Last of England* together, similarly the way he cut his videos for the Pet Shop Boys and the Smiths. When I saw *The Last of England*, I was reacting to something that he was doing that I had originally been influenced by myself—the underground filmmakers of the sixties. For example, you can slow the camera down to two frames a second and project it at that speed so it looks like a NASA space film—click, click, click—or you can make your exposures longer if you shoot in the dark or low-light situations; the images blur out if you pan or zoom around so that they're almost like stills. Derek was doing that kind of thing in his Smiths videos and I was reinfluenced by those techniques when I did videos for the Red Hot Chili Peppers, for example. There are things you do with a Super-8 camera that you don't do with a bigger one.

GF: *In* Drugstore Cowboy *and* My Own Private Idaho, *you made very evocative use of time-lapse photography.*

GVS: Before I finished *Mala Noche*, I taught a time-lapse class. I had done a little time-lapse with Eric Edwards in *The Happy Organ*—a sunrise, going from dark to light, with clouds moving across the sky. Eric had always experimented with time-lapse still photography, like late-night exposures that go on for ten minutes or an hour. I think we even did some experiments in 16mm together. Then he started making these images on his own with an intervelometer he'd made. He sent us a bunch of them during the edit of *Drugstore Cowboy* and I wrote back and told him to shoot specific things that we used in the movie. Then, on *Idaho*, on his own, he was doing these time-lapse shots that weren't in the script and the producer was worried he was using up too much film, but we cut them in for the scenes when Mike blacks out. Before that, we'd make the screen go black but it wasn't working. So Eric's shots became really important as our way of showing an altered sense of time from Mike's perspective. Although Eric continued to shoot some time-lapse stuff during *Cowgirls*, this time we're sort of shying away from them because we've done it enough, I think.

GF: *Going back to* Idaho, *it's central theme is the search for family, specifically, Mike's quest for his mother and Scott's for a father-figure. The movie is dense with references to family. Even in that harrowing scene when Mike visits his brother—who also happens to be his father—you see in the trailer that the brother has all these family portraits from his mail-order photo business.*

GVS: All the stories that I have done so far have had some sort of family metaphor. In *Alice In Hollywood*, the girl falls in with a family of people on the street. In *Mala Noche*, Walt and Pepper form a couple that's more like a father-son relationship, and in *Drugstore Cowboy*, it's like a drug

family. In *Idaho*, it's a street family again with Bob as the father figure, but it's a displaced, temporary family. The film's about *why* Mike's on the street—because his real family didn't work. That comes directly from a number of people that I've known that live that kind of life; in every case, they came from some sort of problematic family situation. One of the kids who I filmed for the interviews in the cafe in *Idaho*, but who didn't make the final cut, was talking about how he had a motorcycle accident and his family was sued for a million dollars and he had to leave because they didn't have the money and blamed him.

In Scott's case, he has a very rigid family order which is cueing off of *Henry IV*. The reason Prince Hal is running around the villages around the castle is because it's his last chance to do that before he has to accept the responsibility of being king—the same with Scott as the mayor's son. Mike's family is cueing off of this Sam Shepard-like family that is eating away at itself. *Cowgirls* is about a girl who is a hitch-hiker, who has this wandering spirit and finds a family on a ranch, a family of women that she ends up staying with.

GF: *Where does all this come from? It is something that you just find affecting, or is it a personal obsession?*

GVS: It's probably a personal thing. Families are interesting stuff. The dynamics of whatever kind of family you have is an orientation that you apply to the outside world. Maybe it's just the most interesting thing that I know. Even the Harvey Milk project was about finding a new family, the Castro Street community being a family of like-minded men who had a new style of relating to one another and had sexual relationships with one another. This was a very clear bond in the new Castro Street of 1975. Almost everything that I have considered doing has some sort of family theme, but you could probably say that about a lot of films.

GF: *Are you aware of autobiographical content in your films?*

GVS: No, I'm not aware of it. I'm not being analytical. I just create everything intuitively. If you're too analytical, what you're doing probably ends up being too specific. I think it's different to the way a lot of people work. I think the more successful painters or photographers or filmmakers or poets sift a lot of different things into one, and aren't analytical and specific and conscious of what they are actually doing. If you have a need to be conscious of what you're doing, that can get in the way of a lot of things happening at the same time, limiting the number of ways that you can express yourself in one image. If you're taking a picture of something and you don't know why you like it, you can sit there for a long time and figure out why. It might take you weeks to figure out why that one image is important. But if you sat there and pre-decided why the image is important, you might never take a picture. You sort of have a hunch why you do something, you know? You see things happening as they are happening, and you might have one reason why you're focusing on that one particular image or action. But then there might be a whole lifetime of reasons why you're focusing on it — and hopefully you are producing images that have a lifetime of meaning in them.

GF: *I guess I was thinking specifically of Scott coming from the middle class, as you did yourself.*

GVS: Well, he's probably me. I can use my own background as an example for Scott's background, and I did sometimes with Keanu, too. Keanu grew up with a well-off background himself and used that when he was figuring out how to play the part. We tried to work out who Scott was. At times he was maybe both of us, Keanu and me. Whereas River had a different background than I had and related more to Mike.

Scott comes from a wealthy family and his father is mayor because Prince Hal came from royalty, and that was the closest thing I could find to royalty in Portland. I think the film might have suffered a little bit from that because there is a difference between being a king and being the mayor's son. The reason Scott's like he is is because of the Shakespeare, and the reason the Shakespeare is in the film is to transcend time, to show that those things have always happened, everywhere. That's why Mike and Scott end up with the boys in the piazza in Rome, which is just like the street scene in Portland.

GF: *Where did the image of the jumping salmon come from?*

GVS: It's a real north-western image. The Columbia river used to be filled with salmon and it's being depleted quite rapidly. The house I live in was built by a salmon canner and cook and I always thought that was a good omen.

GF: *The salmon are jumping upstream, aren't they?*

GVS: Yeah, they're going against the current. That's the central metaphor, in that Mike is essentially trying to find the place where he was conceived. He's also wearing a jacket that's a salmon-coloured pink. So he's the salmon, swimming against the current that is life, and trying to reach his roots, which is his brother. I don't mention it in the film, but the Columbia river runs from Idaho, and when the salmon swim, they swim towards Idaho. So when Mike and Scott are motorcycling from Portland to Idaho they're traveling in the same direction as the salmon. I only just thought of that!

Another thing that occurs to me is that America has a certain culture that's always reverting or trying to figure out where it came from. So we are always going back to the origins of different styles from the Renaissance through different movements in Europe in the 1800s and 1900s. As an American artist, maybe I am also swimming back to relate to some sort of European movement, where I came from, as opposed to American Indian art movements, for example.

One metaphor that was not in the *Idaho* rewrites, that we didn't work on in the final version of the script, was that the boys are supposed to be going toward their ethnic origins, which in their case would be Scotland or Ireland or England, and trying to find a family that had the same last name as they did. As I said before, that was in the original *My Own Private Idaho* story, where these two boys go to Spain, travelling to their ultimate origin, a town that has the same name as one of them.

GF: *Sex in your films is seldom consummated in live action, if at all. For example, in* Drugstore Cowboy, *Bob and Dianne are interrupted by the police when they're about to have sex. In* My Own Private Idaho, *you use montages of stills. Is it too easy an option to show an actual sex scene?*

GVS: I used the photos so that you could see what happened without getting too involved. You could understand it without having to go through a sex scene, which can sometimes be hard to watch and hard to get into—or get through. There's a filmmaker I like who did some still lifes with nudes; the actors were just frozen. That occurred to me as a way to present a sex scene without actually showing it, or the actors smoking in bed afterwards. It was written down that way in the script.

GF: *You referred just now to Native American art as something separate from your own origins, and yet I've noticed bits of American Indian culture cropping up in your films; not only in the character of Julian in* Cowgirls *but also in* Mala Noche *and* My Own Private Idaho, *particularly the Indian war chant that we hear when Mike and Scott are sitting by the fire.*

GVS: That's because they're travelling to Idaho, going through Indian territory. It also says 'Warning To Tourists: Do Not Laugh at the Natives' near the fire. I think that comes from the Warm Springs Indian Reservation in Oregon.

GF: *These things might also signify that there are more ancient rituals underpinning the modernism in your work. It also occurs to me that* Drugstore Cowboy *is a kind of Western.*

GVS: Well, all these stories are really modern Westerns because they're written in the West and take place there. River Phoenix was born in Madras, Oregon, which is right next to that Indian reservation; I didn't know until he told me and I thought it was an amazing coincidence. That road that he stands on in the film is about thirty minutes away from where he was born. His parents travelled from Oregon to California, nomadically, like neo-Westerners that have travelled from the East and come West. Walt Curtis's story in *Mala Noche* is a sort of Western—

Portland is a Western town. Only fifty years ago, Portland had dirt streets. The people that live there are descendants of the original pioneers and of the Indians; you see that very strongly in Ken Kesey's books. My ancestors went as far as Kentucky and settled there, then eventually my parents went to Portland. That kind of history is behind a lot of the characters in the films.

GF: *Finally, on* My Own Private Idaho, *the ending is ambivalent. Mike's lying in the road and someone drives up and takes him away. In the script it says it's Scott who picks him up, but in the film that's not clear. Also, you don't know whether this person is going to save him or hurt him.*

GVS: You're not supposed to know, really. It's like the end of *Drugstore Cowboy,* where people don't know whether Bob dies or survives. Some people have asked me who picks Mike up. In a way, it's either *you* who's the person picking him up or you're *him,* just being asleep. Or it's just a non-ending, and you assume he will go on in his quest. He's a character that has a hard time changing, so he's just going to go on like that forever—wandering and searching.

GF: *In* Even Cowgirls Get the Blues *is there a similar sense that Sissy—the consummate hitch-hiker—is trying to hitch a ride with us?*

GVS: You could look at it that way, though it's not really as pointed as the other films in terms of being told from the character's point of view. Sissy is more of a character apart from the audience's point of view. You are experiencing things along with her, but they're not necessarily told from her perspective. *Mala Noche, Drugstore Cowboy,* and *My Own Private Idaho* are definitely films that are told through the characters' eyes. Less so with Sissy. She's an object that you're watching as opposed to someone you're watching the world through.

GF: *When you came to write the script, how did you go about cutting your way through all of Tom Robbins's riffing on different mythologies and cultural allusions? It couldn't have been an easy novel to condense. What was your guiding principle?*

GVS: There are a lot of things that he just talks about, his own reveries, which are beside the things the characters are doing and talking about. Those went. I followed what the characters were saying, not the things Robbins speaks about.

GF: *Was it a hard job of adaptation?*

GVS: Just going by that rule, it was pretty easy.

GF: *But you did pull in quite a bit of visual minutiae from the book.*

GVS: Only in the descriptions of what things look like and so forth—not literally. There might be some things that I took out of Robbins's mouth and, if it was appropriate, put into one of the character's mouths, but it was pretty rare. There's a little bit of narration in the middle of the movie, and then there's a description of an inanimate object, a brown paper bag, which is from the book, but those are the only things I took directly. Robbins's discussion between the thumb and the brain, that whole thing about using the amoeba as a mascot for the novel— all that I had to leave out.

GF: *Did you invent a lot?*

GVS: No, because there was so much in the book that I had to edit out. It was really an editing job. It usually is when you adapt a novel. *Mala Noche, Drugstore Cowboy,* and then the Shakespeare scenes in *My Own Private Idaho* were all editing jobs and didn't involve too much creation. The non-Shakespeare parts in *Idaho* are the most creative parts of any script I've done. The novels I've adapted gave me really strict guideposts as to what I was doing.

GF: *Was it important for you to stay true to the spirit of Robbins's novel?*

GVS: Yes, and it's hard sometimes to stay true and not get lost. In the case of *Mala Noche,* Walt Curtis was around and he showed us some things that we could do that he remembered doing, that weren't in the book. Then, with *Drugstore Cowboy,* there were a couple of scenes in the book that we hadn't touched on in the script but which we include in the film; sometimes it's just a few lines.

The same with *Cowgirls* where we shot an extra scene from the book, though it didn't make the final cut.

GF: *It was reported in the gossip column of the* New York Post *that you'd cut out a long scene involving the Keanu Reeves character, Julian.*

GVS: The problem was that Julian is only a passing character in the movie. In the novel, there's a whole engaged kind of life that Sissy has with Julian, who is a gentrified Mohawk Indian living in New York. He represents traditional marriage and she ends up marrying him and becoming dissatisfied with her life because she feels pinned down. All this is going on while she's hitch-hiking to the ranch and back again, and eventually he loses her. It was evident when I was writing the script that these were two different stories. There was one at the ranch with Bonanza Jellybean and there was one in New York with Julian. As time went by, we favoured the ranch instead of New York, and the way the script ended up Julian became a less important character.

What happened when we shot the movie was that Keanu found a section of the book that he thought was really interesting, and we worked on it and rehearsed and shot it. It was actually very nice in the movie, but it was a long scene that took away from Cissy's involvement with Jellybean at the ranch because it makes Julian's character larger. It was a close decision in the end. We wanted to keep it in and for a while we did, but eventually we took it out.

GF: *The novel talks a lot of philosophy. What aspect of that were you most keen to get across?*

GVS: I think my attraction to *Cowgirls* is that it's a kind of New Age novel. It was, as Robbins wrote it, setting up a new bunch of rules as to how to tell a story, and it mixed in a lot of different techniques on top of one another. That was what really struck me. It also plays with a couple of different genres, one of them being the romance novel. It seemed Robbins was using the form of the romance novel to write a new fiction. He has the lead character going in and out of different sexual situations to

create this very grand, *Gone with the Wind* type of journey. As she's a hitch-hiker, it could also be a road movie, which I think my other movies are, too, including *Mala Noche*, although I read *Cowgirls* before I read *Mala Noche* or considered any of the other movies. There were a lot of really exciting, unexpected storytelling elements that inspired me to turn *Cowgirls* into a script. It'd take too long to describe specifically what the message of the movie is because there's a lot of different characters who explain their philosophies of life and Sissy experiences each different one. Then she has her own philosophy, which is just to keep moving. I don't know if there is any one specific idea, except maybe 'time' itself, rhythm itself, is a kind of metaphor within the overall scheme of the movie. Time measured by travel, distance, practices; time measured by literal time, historical time, philosophical time, or religious time.

GF: *What were your feelings about the camp, over-the-top country-and-western ambiance of the novel?*

GVS: The campiness and the irreverent quality is, I think, a philosophy of life that comes from Robbins himself—like, don't take things too seriously.

GF: *Do you regard your film of* Cowgirls *as a kind of non-ideological feminist film, in the same way that* My Own Private Idaho *could be described as a non-ideological gay film?*

GVS: No, not really—they're almost opposite. Although *Idaho* has characters that are perhaps gay and perhaps not, I don't think it's specifically talking about homosexuality. The boys are making money from sex, usually with men, but the film doesn't have any kind of backbone that makes it a gay film as such; except that it was made by me. *Cowgirls* has a much more organized sort of agenda, presenting philosophies that are feminist. Maybe *Idaho* is a non-gay film made by a gay director and *Cowgirls* is a feminist film adapted from a book by a non-feminist or a non-female writer, Robbins, and also directed by a man: me. The philosophies and the discussions in *Cowgirls* are extremely pro-feminist or pro-female, and pro new life.

There're all kinds of things that go on within it that address that.

GF: *Reading the script, I thought of it as an estrogen movie because it repudiates feminine-hygiene sprays and celebrates female juices in all their olfactory power.*

GVS: It's also part of those times, the seventies, when there was an insistence on feminine hygiene. Body odours and feminine odours, in particular, were to be covered up. At the time, the Food and Drug Administration had found problems with the hygienes that were being marketed. This is why there's a character, the Countess, who owns a feminine-hygiene company that has a staff of females who are standing up and speaking for themselves, and overthrowing the beauty ranch because of the products it's making. The book is very hippie-esque in its point of view: let the body smell the way it smells.

GF: *The Countess [John Hurt] is a misogynistic gay 'queen'. Are you prepared for a certain amount of flak over the way he's been depicted?*

GVS: I'm sure the Countess will cause some sort of an outburst. Harvey Milk himself was accused of being a misogynist by a large number of lesbians, and gay men were often viewed as misogynistic towards the lesbian community, even though they were after the same ends. I'm prepared for some outrage, though—once again—the tone of the film is: Don't take things too seriously. If people want to take a caricature like that seriously, then that's their problem. There's a famous Marcel Duchamp quote that we use in Delores del Ruby's speech when she addresses the cowgirls' extreme position in harbouring the endangered whooping cranes as a ransom to allow them to keep the ranch for themselves. She says: 'Playfulness ceases to serve a purpose when it takes itself too seriously.'

GF: *Would you describe* Cowgirls *as generally lighter in tone than your other films?*

GVS: I think it's much lighter, though it's not quite as dreamy as the others. There are things in the novel that are a lot more fanciful and surrealistic than in the film, because we had to make them seem a little bit more real.

GF: *As in all your films, it has a ritual sacrifice in which someone dies. It was Pepper in* Mala Noche, *Nadine in* Drugstore Cowboy, *Scott's father and Bob in* My Own Private Idaho, *and now Bonanza Jellybean in* Even Cowgirls Get the Blues. *This would have obviously continued if you'd done the Harvey Milk film,* The Mayor of Castro Street.

GVS: Maybe in writing something where you are trying to explore the extremes of certain situations, sometimes the characters that die provoke the other characters that remain alive to change, and often it's meant to do that. In the film of *Mala Noche*, Pepper dies as a result of the immigration raid. Sometimes there are shoot-outs in those situations. In the novel, Pepper simply disappears; he was rounded up. I made him die to communicate the seriousness of the plight of migrant workers. They are more in danger on the Mexican border, obviously, than in Portland, Oregon, but that kind of death is more a reality to Johnny and Pepper than it is to the other people on the street in *Mala Noche*. In that particular film, that was something that I constructed. In the book, Walt didn't know whether he'd died or not until he resurfaced later.

In *Drugstore Cowboy*, Nadine's death is an emblematic drug death from an overdose, which was really common to the life that Fogle lived and an amalgamation of a lot of different things that had happened in his career as a robber and a junkie; it wasn't based on a specific person. In *Idaho*, the death of Scott's father echoes the death of the king in *Henry IV*, and it's mirrored by the death of Bob: Falstaff, too, dies in Shakespeare. So in that case, it came from the plays, and we used it to sum up the duality of the father figures. In *Cowgirls*, Jelly's death is the death of a traditional heroine, giving birth to the future of the rest of the cowgirls.

Harvey Milk's dying was one of the things that made them think about making that movie originally. Maybe it's similar to the deaths in the other films, but the way I would have done it would have been to show him as a martyr for the gay movement. He became stronger, and the movement became stronger, because of his assassination. I would have had him as a larger, straight-on hero than the characters in the other films who are more like anti-heroes.

GF: *You made* Cowgirls *for $8.5 million, by far and away your biggest budget. With all that money, did you find that you had to make adjustments in how you directed it?*

GVS: We had more time to do stuff; though we had a smaller crew than we did on *Drugstore Cowboy*. I haven't really run into the sort of thing that could have happened if I'd made the Harvey Milk film or in a situation where there's a lot of studio involvement.

GF: *Are you satisfied with the films you've made so far?*

GVS: I think in most cases I've been pretty surprised by the end result of the films. When you're working on them, you're always losing ground and gaining ground. You lose some things and gain some things when you're shooting. Then, when you're editing, you're not sure how it's going to turn out. *Alice In Hollywood* had been a really big disappointment; that just crushed me. But maybe it was good that the first one wasn't successful—I probably learned from that. So far I've been happy with the other films and the responses to them. Yeah, so far.

Foreword

Printed in this volume is the screenplay *My Own Private Idaho*, untouched and in its original form before filming began. We chose to publish it this way as opposed to printing a transcript of the finished movie so that one could better see the process of change that a project goes through before it reaches the audience. During shooting, the actors, cinematographers, and I would freely change things, adding scenes or shots, deleting them, and ad libbing lines or action.

One particular scene, the famous one around the campfire in *My Own Private Idaho*, was reworked by River Phoenix a great deal. River found this scene a pivotal point for his character and encouraged me to allow him to change his dialogue so he could express things that were not in the screenplay. I think you will find an interesting difference from the way the character of 'Mike' was written, and the direction in which River finally took him.

During the editing of the film, the editor and I mixed things around a great deal. This usually happens on my films, so that the end product differs greatly from the original intent. As the script of *Idaho* was forged, the ending had a variety of people picking 'Mike' up from the road as he lay unconscious. In the script printed here there is a specific person who picks him up, but in the film the identity of this person is hidden, so that viewers can make up their own ending.

Also during *Idaho*, Eric Edwards, one of our two cinematographers, had been shooting a lot of time-lapse views of mountains, clouds, roads, and such. Our producer, Laurie Parker, was having trouble justifying all the money that was being spent on the film stock that Eric had been using, but by the time the film was finished, I had fitted these shots into the movie to help River's character in his narcoleptic states. In the end, the time-lapse shots had become the secret meaning of the movie. They had become the Private Idaho of the title. However, this was only something that we came up with in the editing room, and so these shots and meanings are not in the screenplay.

The typeface of the original screenplay is a sort of patchwork I arrived at with my Apple computer. It was submitted this way and worked on by all departments in this form. The film *Idaho* began with an unusual screenplay and everything that happened after that was a direct result of the way that it looked when people first read it. It is unconventional enough to have turned off a lot of people in the 'business' simply because those people were in the 'business' of conformity, as is most of Hollywood. I am not. To me this is extremely significant.

Gus Van Sant
June 1993

my oWN

PRIvaTe

idAHo

a screenplay   by   Gus Van Sant

revised Apr. '89

My Own Private Idaho was first shown at the Venice Film Festival in 1991. The cast includes:

MIKE WATERS	River Phoenix
SCOTT FAVOR	Keanu Reeves
RICHARD WATERS	James Russo
BOB PIGEON	William Reichert
GARY	Rodney Harvey
CARMELLA	Chiara Caselli
DIGGER	Michael Parker
DENISE	Jessie Thomas
BUDD	Flea
ALENA	Grace Zabriskie
JACK FAVOR	Tom Troupe
HANS	Udo Kier
JANE LIGHTWORK	Sally Curtice
WALT	Robert Lee Pitchlynn
DADDY CARROLL	Mickey Cottrell
WADE	Wade Evans
Directors of Photography	Eric Alan Edwards
	John Campbell
Editor	Curtiss Clayton
Production Designer	David Brisbin
Costume Designer	Beatrix Aruna Pasztor
Music	Bill Stafford
Executive Producer	Gus Van Sant
Co-executive Producer	Allan Mindel
Producer	Laurie Parker
Screenplay	Gus Van Sant
	Additional dialogue by
	William Shakespeare
Director	Gus Van Sant

Produced by New Line Cinema

VIEWS OF THE CITY OF Portland Oregon *digressing into
the seedy areas of the small city.*
*ARCADES, and yellow storefronts, of PORNOGRAPHIC
BOOKSHOPS.*

*A FEW YOUNG MEN LOITER IN FRONT OF ONE OF THE
BOOKSHOPS SOLICITOUSLY AND EYE A CUSTOMER.*

WHO ENTERS THE BOOKSHOP.

INSIDE, WE SEE:
Counters displaying COLORFUL COMIC–LIKE plastic covered
MAGAZINE and BOOK COVERS with names like HONCHO
– BUTCH – JOYBOY. INDICATING A Homo–erotic section
of the bookshop.

GROUPS OF MEN loiter about the magazine shop flipping
through the books and disappearing in and out of
curtained doors.

THE COUNTERMAN is on the phone.

Next to him is a particularly interesting YOUNG MAN on
the cover of one of the magazines – a bright yellow
background, jeans open two buttons on the top,
shirtless wearing a black cowboy hat. This character is
named SCOTT.

FULL VIEW of the MAGAZINE cover as Scott comes to life
– and talks to us.

                    SCOTT
    *I never thought I could be a real model, you know
    fashion–shit, cause I'm better at full body stuff.
    It's okay so long as the photographer doesn't come
    on to you and expect something for no pay. I'm
    trying to make a living, you know, and I like to be
    professional. 'Course if the guy wants to pay me,*

SCOTT (continued)
then shit/yeah. Here I am for him. I'll sell my
ass, I do it on the street all the time for cash.
And I'll be on the cover of a book. It's when you
start doing it for free that you start to grow wings,
Right, Mike?

ACROSS THE AISLE ON ANOTHER SHELF IS ANOTHER
COVER OF A MAGAZINE, AND ANOTHER YOUNG MAN ON
THE COVER STARTS TO MOVE AND SPEAK, ADDRESSING
SCOTT.

This character is named MIKE. (MIKE SHOULD BE
DIFFERENT FROM SCOTT, MIKE SHOULD BE BLOND AND
SCOTT SHOULD BE BROWN HAIRED, ALTHOUGH BOTH
POSSESS A CERTAIN PAINFUL DOWN AND OUT
HANDSOMENESS OF A STREET HUSTLER.)

MIKE
What are you talking about.   What wings?

SCOTT
Wings, man, you grow wings and become a
FAIRY.

MIKE
I ain't no fairy.

ANOTHER COVERBOY INTERRUPTS MIKE AND SCOTT'S
DISCUSSION, BUTTING IN.

COVERBOY
He ain't saying you is a fairy, faggot, he's
saying that if you go working for free then you
has no choice, you turn into a fairy, with
wings and all. That's all he mean, dunk.

MIKE (to Scottie)
Well, nevertheless, what do you care about
doing stuff for free or for money, shit. You're
going to inherit a bunch of money, you might
as well do it for free.

5

COVERBOY
Is that right, sweetie?

*OTHER COVERBOYS PERK UP AND START FLIRTING WITH
SCOTT.*

COVERBOY 2
How much is a bunch of money, honey?

COVERBOY 3
*What are you doing on the cover of that
magazine, slumming?*

Scott listens to all of them then looks back at Mike.

Mike smiles.

SCOTT
(to us)

*Actually, I'm on the street to settle a bet with
my goddamned stone-faced old man. I've
decided to live away from home for three
years. To prove a point. That I can live on
my own. And to appreciate the value of a
dollar. And Mike is right, there, I am going to
inherit money. A lot of money.*

I d A h o

The desert in the daytime.
MIKE enters the frame in front of a blue sky filled with white clouds. He has a Texaco gas station attendant's shirt on with a name tag that reads: BILL (not Mike, his name).

The clouds are puffy against a deep blue sky. The road is red. Purple mountains surround Mike on all sides far in the distance, ten miles away. Mike looks in front of him at a long stretch of road that disappears into the horizon.

Mike looks at his wristwatch on his arm. He times how long it takes to walk ten steps down the road.
Ten seconds. He glances back at a duffle bag. The duffle bag falls over.

Mike looks at the picturesque sights surrounding him. A wind sends a tumbleweed into the air. He takes ten steps back to his duffle bag and checks watch again.

The sun is now setting.

                    MIKE
          (to himself)
     You can always tell where you are by the way
     the road looks. Like I just know that I been to
     this place before. I just know that I been
     stuck here like this one fuckin' time before,
     you know that?

ON THE SIDE OF THE ROAD A JACKRABBIT IS LISTENING
TO HIM.

> MIKE
> There ain't no other road on earth that looks
> like this road. I mean, exactly like this road.
> (sniffs)
> One of a kind. (Sniffs) Like someone's face.
> Like a fucked up face...

THE ROAD HAS A DEFINITE FACE. TWO DISTANT CACTUS
FOR EYES - A CLOUD SHADOW FOR A MOUTH, MOUNTAINS
FOR HAIR.

> MIKE
> Once you see it, even for a second, you
> remember it, and you better not forget it, you
> gotta remember people and who they are,
> right? Friends and enemies. You gotta
> remember the road and where it is too...

MIKE SUDDENLY LUNGES AT THE LITTLE RABBIT
LISTENING TO HIS CHAT ON THE SIDE OF THE ROAD, AND
THE RABBIT RUNS FOR HIS LIFE.

> MIKE
> I just love to scare things...I don't know. It
> gives me a sense of....Power.

Mike thinks about the loneliness of the road.

> MIKE
> This is nowhere. I'll bet that nobody is ever
> going to drive down this road. I'll be stuck
> here forever.

Mike looks at the road stressfully. The road looks back.
He looks at the road.....his eyes growing heavy. The
road looks back...

Mikes yawns.

> MIKE'S VOICE OVER
> I don't know when it was I recognized I had
this disease.

Mike looks like a backwoods character who fits into the terrain. Mike makes strange movements, like he is having a sort of epileptic fit, then yawns like he is very tired, again.

> MIKE'S VOICE OVER
> Sometimes I'll be in one place, and I'll close my eyes...

MIKE CLOSES HIS EYES. THEN A WHOLE RITUAL OF EVENTS HAPPENS, HIS EYES TURN BACK IN HIS HEAD AND HE BEGINS TO SHAKE ALL OVER. THEN ALL GOES BLACK.

> MIKE'S VOICE OVER
> When I open them again, I'll be in a completely different surrounding.

When Mike opens his eyes, he is in downtown PORTLAND, OREGON.

A LOUD BUS drives by Mike's view in the city. He is asleep, then wakes enough to see other UNKNOWN KIDS rifling his pockets in a doorway, as Mike sleepily looks on.

> SUBTITLES
> It's kind of like time travel. It's kind of good.

MIKE CLOSES HIS EYES AGAIN, AND WHEN HE OPENS THEM HE IS BACK IN THE COUNTRY. BUT THIS TIME A COMPLETELY DIFFERENT TERRAIN. LIKE A LONG TIME HAS PASSED. HE IS ALSO WEARING DIFFERENT CLOTHES.

MIKE CHECKS HIS WATCH AGAIN. He looks happy at the passage of time.

> MIKE
> Yeah. It's kind of good. Passes the time. Unwanted as it is.

9

MIKE LEANS AGAINST THE DUFFLE BAG WITH HIM. HE
LOOKS INTO THE FIELD next to him. The wind blows a
paper cup into the air.

Mike watches the cup tumble in the air, and with a few
notes, a GUITAR follows. Then an uprooted cactus.

The paper cup, cactus and guitar lyrically trade places
in the air, and are followed by a large barn, which
twists and turns, then crashes directly into the middle
of the road.

On the road. *Riding in the back of a pickup truck.*
Mike's shirt ruffles wildly in the wind, traveling at 60
mph.

And the truck disappears into the sun, toward a steep
mountain range.

10

L A S   V E G A S

O

*M*ike is walking down a LONELY ALLEYWAY in the
city. ALL OF A SUDDEN he is surrounded by three
BLACK BOYS, who are smiling and joking.

                    BLACK 1
          SAY, WHITE BOY, where you goin'?

Black 1 pulls out a knife and waves it at Mike.

                    BLACK 1
          What's in the sack. Let's see.

Mike fights with the guy for his sack. The Black cuts
Mike's hands with his knife but Mike won't let go.

In terror he watches his hands get cut, but he won't let
go. Mike starts to yawns and does the jitters to the
Black's amazement and drops to the ground. Scottie,
the older boy on the magazine cover, comes to Mike's
aid. He pushes the Black boy over, throws some trash
cans in their direction.

                    BLACK 1
          This gonna be fun. Come on...

Scottie keeps fighting them off.

                    SCOTTIE
          Man, what do you want from us, we haven't
          got anything.

The Blacks chuckle. Then they stop and slowly walk
away from Scott who hovers protectively around Mike's
body on the ground.

                        BLACK (o.s.)
        Faggot!

We are in the city of Las Vegas in the daytime. (We are
aware of this because one character, RAY, is reading
the Las Vegas Chronicle.) —Mike sleeps, as a shopkeeper
washes his windows and three other street kids, Gary,
Ray and Scottie, are hanging around on the corner with
him.

Gary is hitting a public wastebasket with the end of a
stick as a MAN in a MERCEDES BENZ drives by them
very slowly, and looks at each one of the boys
individually. Gary pauses for a moment and poses.

                        RAY
                (to the man in the car)
            What's up?

                        MAN (in German)
            [*Entschuldiging, junge...*]

The man in the car speeds off.

INT. CAR DAY.

THE MAN has the look of Rainer Fassbinder and Geraldo
Rivera as the same man; is of average build and has a
wash of hair gracing his forehead that looks quite
foreign. He turns to the right three times, as he is
circling his car.

OUT THE WINDOW OF THE CAR, we see the boys again.

EXT. STREET
                        GARY
            What's this guy want, think he wants to
            party?

                            12

                    SCOTT
He said "Entschuldiging, junge."

                    GARY
What's that mean? "Suck my dick?" Does he
want to suck my dick?

                    SCOTT
It means, "Excuse me, boys."

                    GARY
How the fuck do you know.

                    SCOTT
I've studied German, in prep school.

                    GARY
You know, Scottie, I don't know when to
believe you.

                    SCOTT
Here he comes again.

THE MAN leans out the window of his car.

                    MAN
            HELLO?

Gary leans into the man's car.

                    GARY
            Hey, dude.

                    MAN
            (speaks with a thick German accent)
Excuse me. Can I speak to the young man over
there, with the blond hair, ya?

                    GARY
Who, that kid there? You can't talk with him
now, he's asleep.

> MAN
> Can you wake him up?

> GARY
> No, you can't wake him...he's....but, what
> about me? Don't you want to talk with me?

The man is not interested in talking to Gary.

He shakes his head no, bothered by Gary.

> SCOTT
> (speaking fluent German)
> *Was willst du in Gottesname mit uns Juenge?*
> *Mach' es klar oder fahre ab!*
> (What in the hell do you want with us
> young kids, be specific or get out.)

> MAN
> (surprised)
> *Du bisst sehr intelligent mit deinem Aksent...*
> *Fuer einen Puppejunge.*
> (You are very clever with an accent like
> that..for a street boy.)

THE MAN IN THE CAR SPEEDS OFF.

> GARY
> Alright then, asshole!

VIEW of Mike's sleeping face.

INSIDE OF MIKE's thoughts. He is flying over the city
streets, *above the Mercedes Benz, effortlessly hovering*
and gliding above it, between the buildings. Like a
bird.

MIke wakes and looks at Scottie, who is talking to
Gary.

MIKE'S THOUGHTS

The first time I met Scott, I had a feeling he
was a sort of comic book hero. He was always
saying the right thing at the right moment,
and standing up for me when there was no
reason to. Look at his face now, when the
sunlight shines off his lower lip, like it is the
face of some sort of statue. Strong and soft at
the same time. I never could figure out what
Scott was doing here with us on the street in
the first place, like he was on some sort of
crusade, to help the poor. Because he really
did come from a rich Portland family. I know
because he brought me to his house one day
and showed me around. I mean, wow, they
were rich! They even had a swimming pool.
Scott's the only kid that I had ever met that
had a swimming pool. I'd make a bet with
anybody right now, that Scott is a saint or a
hero, or some such higher placed person.

Meanwhile...

*Gary and Ray are talking. Ray, who is a Chicano
street kid, is looking poetically off into the distance.*

RAY

My father was a gaucho. But nobody gonna
find him. He killed a guy and split. Nobody
gonna find that fuck. I never gonna find him.

*Ray spits into the gutter and the spit drifts in a small
stream made by the shop-owner who was washing his
windows, down the street and into a drainage grating.*

View of MIKE as he closes his eyes, oblivious to what is
going on around him.

The music in a DISCO blares, at night, and all we can
see is Mike's face, sleeping. The disco MUSIC STOPS, and
the lights go up.

15

A broom passes by Mike's head.

Finally, THE MANAGER'S SHOES appear at his head.

> MANAGER (o.s.)
> What's wrong with him?   Passed out?

The shoes prod Mike.

> MANAGER (o.s.)
> Hey, wake up.

Mike wakes up in a WARD ROOM BED in the daytime. He looks around him. The room has a lot of light, windows practically on all sides of the room.   There are other DETOX men and women in other beds.   Mike gets up and starts to walk out, but he is wearing a gown.

A nurse stops him.

> NURSE
> Excuse me.   Are you all right?

> MIKE
> Yeah.   I'm fine. (Mike looks around the room.)

> NURSE
> If you're going to leave us, it's okay, but we need you to sign out, and you'll need to get your clothes from downstairs.

> MIKE
> Oh.   Yeah. (he pauses and looks around the place.)
> Do you live here?

> NURSE
> Why...no.   But sometimes I feel like I do.

The nurse walks him over to a clipboard on a desk. Mike signs the board, and she gives him a receipt.

                    MIKE
        What's this?

                    NURSE
        That's just a receipt.   You can throw it away
        if you don't want it.   That's what most people
        do with it.

Then we cut to Mike's face at night. As his eyes open
he takes a look around him, a little dazed, trying to
figure where he is. We see he is under a store awning.
A lot of fog is rolling across the street.

A twenty-eight-year-old woman stops in a Mercedes
Benz sedan, similar to the one that the German man
was driving. She motions Mike to get inside the car.

Dazed, Mike looks at the car, then responds.

                    MIKE
        This chick is living in a new car ad.

Inside a hallway entrance to the woman's home, Mike
and the woman take off their jackets.

                    MIKE
        This is like a dream. A pretty woman never
        picks me up.

Mike begins to caress her arm.

                    LADY
        They Don't? Well. I Don't see why not...

                    MIKE
        Is this your house?

                    LADY (caressing his head)
        Yes...

                            17

Mike follows the woman into her...

Living room where sit Scottie and Gary on a plush
sofa. Mike sees them.

                    MIKE
        Oh...

Mike sits down in an easy chair next to the sofa.

                    MIKE
        What's up, Gary? Scottie?

                    GARY
        HEY, DUDE.

                    LADY
        You men make yourselves comfortable, and I'll
        be right back. There're cokes in the
        refrigerator - help yourself.

They watch her go.

                    SCOTTIE
        She's cool. She just likes to have three guys,
        'cause - it takes her a little while to get
        warmed up. It's normal. Nothing kinky.

                    MIKE
        Oh.

Mike looks around the room. Gary leans closer to
Mike.

                    GARY
        Hey, did you get into that Van Halen concert
        last night?

                    MIKE
        I've never been to a concert, dude.

Interior of the Woman's bedroom. Mike undresses. He waits by the side of the bed and takes a last drag on a cigarette and puts it out. Then the woman arrives, lets down her negligé and approaches Mike like an EARTH MOTHER, slowly, big breasted, warm, comforting.

As she approaches, Mike begins to see a familiar face. He is upset when he looks into her eyes. And he begins to spasmodically shake then he grows sleepy, and finally, as she is upon him, he passes out.

Outside, Gary and Scottie struggle with Mike's body.

They plop Mike down on the corner, under a streetlight, fold his arms under his stomach and bend him over so he is sitting up against the light pole.

> SCOTT
> (putting money into his pocket)
> He always does this! I'm surprised he makes money at all.

> GARY
> How do we tell if he's okay?

> SCOTT
> Well, he's not dead.

Scott listens to his heart.

> SCOTT
> Listen.

Gary listens.

> SCOTT
> He's not dead. He's just passed out. It's a condition. It's called narcolepsy.

> GARY
> Scared the shit out of her. What causes it. Sex?

19

                    SCOTT
        Stress. Some hustler, huh?

Silence for a second.

                    GARY
        Where are we going to take him?

Scott lifts Mike's body up and carries him to a soft
carpet of grass on the edge of a lawn. Scott looks
around to see if it is okay. Then he speaks to Mike
even though he is asleep.

                    SCOTT
         Hey, little brother. You stay here, and when
         you wake up, just come back into town. I'll
         be there waiting for you. I figure you're going
         to be safer here in this comfy neighborhood
         than in the city. I grew up in a neighborhood
         like this. It'll be safe here.

Scottie hides a tear. Then he takes his jacket off and
puts it over Mike, then leaves him there.

*M*ike's face is lying down with his nose pressed
against a leafy ground in the daytime.

He wakes up, stands, makes his way up a slope and
out to the street. He brushes himself off as the
Mercedes Benz shows up again. Mike recognizes it, and
walks up to the window of the car. It is the MAN,
though, not the lady. The Man speaks with a German
accent – and he is about 35 years old. HIS NAME IS
HANS.

                    MIKE
        Hi.

                        Hans
        Say....

Hans reads Mike's shirt.

                        20

                                    Hans
              Say, Bill.   What's happening?

**Mike brushes himself off and walks down the road,
thinking that the guy is weird.**

                                    MIKE
              Nothing much.

Hans drives alongside Mike in his car.

                                    Hans
              Do you want a lift?   Bill?

                                    MIKE
              Hey, isn't this the lady's car?

                                    Hans
              Is Alena a friend of yours?   She's a friend of
              mine.   Any friend of Alena's is a friend of
              mine.   Do you want to be my friend?

                                    MIKE
              Not really.

                                    Hans
              Get in and I'll take you someplace.   Yes?
              Where do you want to go?

Mike doesn't respond, and walks on.

**He pauses a moment, and looks at the houses in the
neighborhood.   He looks down the street and can see
Hans stopped in his car.   The guy gets out, and leans
against the car.**

                                    MIKE
              This guy is a pervert.   I can tell.

To Hans:

                                    MIKE
              Go home!

THE HOUSES LINE THE STREET, EACH WITH A LITTLE
CALIFORNIA STYLE GARDEN. MIKE CAN SEE ALL THE
ROOFS OF THE HOUSES LIFT OFF, AND THE FURNITURE
INSIDE EACH HOUSE FLY OUT AND CIRCLE IN THE AIR.
MIKE GETS THE JITTERS AND PASSES OUT.

THE MERCEDES BENZ PULLS UP NEXT TO HIS HEAD, WHICH
IS NOW ON THE GROUND.

POR t LA n d

When Mike wakes up he is in Scottie's arms. They sit under a statue in a park. The statue is of two Indians pointing out across the horizon, and on the base of the statue is written: *The Coming of the White Man*.

Mike looks at Scott and then at the new surroundings.

At the Broadway Cafe Mike bites into a hamburger.

> MIKE
> How'd we get home?

> SCOTT
> That German guy. Hans. He brought you downtown, you were passed out. He said he was heading to Portland, so I asked him for a ride.

> MIKE
> I don't remember any German guy.

> SCOTT
> Well. You were sleeping.

> MIKE
> How much do you make off me while I'm sleeping?

> SCOTT
> Just a ride, Mike. I don't make anything. What, you think that I sell your body while you are asleep.

> MIKE
> Yeah.

Scott sips from a coffee cup.

                    SCOTT
          No, Mike. I'm on your side.

He puts down the cup. Mike knows Scottie always tells
the truth. Mike is a little embarrassed, that he has
maybe offended Scott's honor.

                    MIKE
          I was just kidding, dude.

                    SCOTT
          Gary's up here somewhere. He left three days
          ago, he flew up with some John.

                    MIKE
          Exotic. Have you seen your dad?

                    SCOTT
          Are you kidding?

                    MIKE
          I'd visit my dad, if he was here.

                    SCOTT
          I have to take care of you.

                    MIKE
          How about your mom?

                    SCOTT
          No.

                    MIKE
          That lady. She looked like. My mother.

                    SCOTT
          Is that why you passed out?

                    MIKE
          Yeah. I mean. I don't know. She really
          looked like my mother. I must have been
          imagining things.

A pause.

The Broadway Cafe is beginning to pick up in business.
The table where Scott and Mike sit is in front of a large
window, and it is semi-circular in shape. Scottie spies
Gary across the street.

He bounds up out of his chair and Mike watches him as
he goes to the door, kicks it open and yells to Gary.

> SCOTT
> *HEY! You dick!!*

Gary sees Scott and runs across the street.

*L*ater in the BROADWAY CAFE, there are other street
kids hanging around the table.

Scott has his arm around a girl named DENISE, who has
a lot of make up on and long stringy hair and who
carries a teddy bear. Denise is crying and Scott is
consoling her.

> MIKE'S THOUGHTS:
> It was almost as if Scott was on some sort of
> crusade or mission, when you checked him
> out.   He could make you feel good right at the
> very time that you felt so bad. I remember
> there were many times that I had been
> sobbing in Scott's arms and he was helping me
> out too. He was the great protector of us all,
> and the great planner. He gave us hope in the
> future. Even though there was no future.
> There must have been real trouble at home,
> though, for Scott not to want to visit his
> father.

Scott strokes Denise's hair adoringly and gives her a kiss
every now and then.

Mike looks across the table at CARL, a skinny kid with black hair and a large floppy sports cap, and GARY, who is talking with him.

> MIKE'S THOUGHTS
> That's Carl. He's always around the Broadway, he didn't run away from home like a lot of these kids did. He had a mom, and no dad, at least they didn't know where he was. And one day, he came home to the apartment where they lived, and there was no mom anymore either. He didn't know where she went. That was six months ago.

MARY, an older, wiser street prostitute who is chain smoking Kool cigarettes.

> MIKE'S THOUGHTS
> That's Mary over there. She was a mean old chick. She was maybe thirty now. Old, old. Somebody once told me that in the past, Mary had this enemy, a chick that had turned her in. And Mary had gone off and kicked this chick to death right in the street in front of everybody. I don't know if it's true, but I watched out, just in case. I was afraid of Mary. And everyone else was too.

Mary takes a drag from her cigarette and blows smoke in Mike's face.

Scott notices this. But he attends to Denise's problems.

> MIKE's THOUGHTS
> (as he coughs)
> This was our little round table, a point around which everything else revolved. It was our "center." It was like our home. Our living room. Not everyone was the best of friends, but everyone knew everyone else, and we kind of stuck together.

*M*ike on the street. He watches as a man carrying a large bag of tin cans, crosses at a crosswalk. Mike steps up to him and begins walking. His name is MARTY.

MIKE

Hey Marty. What's goin' on?

MARTY

Is that you Mike? Hey, what's new with you? You look pretty good.

MIKE

How many you got so far today?

MARTY

I reckon that I picked up about twenty-three bucks so far with these cans, and some I got stashed back in the bushes. You know the old hiding place?

MIKE

Wow!

MARTY

Don't tell anybody, though. Just between you and me. You need a place to stay?

MIKE

I always need a place to stay, dude.

MARTY

Yeah, well, I'm under the bridge. You can join me if you like.

MIKE

Yeah, I think I'll rooftop it tonight. I'm hanging with a friend.

MARTY

Am I walking too fast for you?

MIKE

No, but I'll see you around. See you under the bridge.

MARTY

Okay, Mike.

Mike stops walking with the guy and he splits down the street at a fast clip.

*I*nside the BROADWAY CAFE, Mike smokes a cigarette at the round table and watches Gary and Carl playing keep-away with Denise's teddy bear. Denise is swearing, using profanities that are unusual for a girl.

*N*ight. Mike walks through a dark wet troubled inner-city alley and on the other side, there is a parked car. In the car sits a man in his 40's, bestial, good looking but overweight. He beeps his car horn at Mike.

Mike pauses, lights a cigarette coolly and walks to the car and leans in the window.

                    MIKE
          Hey – what's up?

*I*nt. MOTEL, nightime.

The man is naked in the background standing in front of a mirror in a motel bathroom, as Mike sits naked on a bed in front of a t.v. set laughing at the show that is on.

We see various *still compositions* of the two making love.

A field. Day. Two figures cross the field. One is Bob Pigeon, a man in his fifties, and the other, his manservant, Budd. Because of his girth, Bob has problems crossing the field.

                    BUDD
          Jesus...the things we've seen...do you
          remember a thing since we moved from
          graffitti bridge?

                    BOB
No more of that, Budd.

                    BUDD
Ha-ha, what a crazy night.

*W*ay above the two walking figures, Gary wakes near
a heating duct atop a ten story building. He yawns,
looks down at the street and spies Bob and Budd.

GARY'S VIEW: a tiny Bob and Budd are making their
way across a field.

                    GARY
      Hey, Scottie, here comes that fat pig himself!!!
      He owes me money!

Scottie, atop an adjacent building peeks his head over
the edge. The two guys are relatively close to one
another but far from the street.

                    SCOTT
Who?

                    GARY
      You know, the fat one...Pigeon!

                    SCOTT
He stole my shoes, the dick!

                    GARY
      Hey, everybody, here comes Bob the chisler!

He yells to the other buildings and other street kids to
wake up. Scottie pours an old paper cup of Coca-Cola
over Bob and Budd below.

                    GARY
      Look out, it's raining Coke!

Bob hears the show atop the buildings.

                         29

> **BOB**
> Ah, I think my friends can see I am back from
> Boise.

Bob looks worried and happy at the same time, not
knowing if they are friend or foe. He shields himself
from the Coke sprinkles.

> **BOB**
> Do you see any clouds in the sky, Budd?

> **BUDD**
> No, Bob.

The Derelict Hotel.

Budd and Bob enter the threshold of a busted up but
operating hotel. There is a fire in a trashcan turned
upside down, with holes poked in it.

Budd looks around the hotel.

> **BUDD**
> Is Jane Lightwork alive, Bob?

> **BOB**
> She's alive, Budd.

> **BUDD**
> Is she holding on?

> **BOB**
> Old...old, Budd.

> **BUDD**
> She must be old, she has no choice...

THE TWO sit at a larger fire deeper into the derelict
hotel.

BUDD

I remember her daughter, she died years
ago...of old age. She must be old, all right.
That was before I came to Clements Inn.

BOB
(warming by the fire)
Ahh...

BUDD

Jesus...the things that we've seen. Aren't I
right, Bob? Aren't I right?

BOB

We have seen the light at the end of the
tunnel...

BUDD

That we have, that we have...in fact Bob, we
have. Jesus...the things that we've seen.

$\mathcal{S}$cott drinks from a beer can inside the derelict hotel,
tosses it to a young boy, laughs, wipes his mouth and
puts his lit cigarette into the mouth of Gary, making
his way to some steps, through a circle of girls, kisses
Denise, who we remember from the Broadway Cafe, and
charges up the steps.

Inside the hotel on a staircase landing, Scottie passes a
couple of figures, one is asleep and one is awake.

SCOTTIE
Where's Bob?

A BOY
Fast asleep.

BUDD
And he's snoring like a horse.

SCOTTIE OPENS A DOOR AT THE TOP OF THE STEPS AND
WALKS INTO A ROOM, INTERRUPTING MIKE, WHO STANDS
OVER BOB'S SNORING BODY.

Mike coolly holds up a wad of bills and a folded envelope
of cocaine.

                    MIKE
          I picked his pocket.

                    SCOTTIE (whispering)
          What did you get, dude?

                    MIKE
          Just this.

Scottie takes the cocaine from him, sits down at the
foot of the bed and begins to undold the packet. Bob
turns in the bed and the rush of air from the sheets
blows the white powder out of the packet.

                    BOB
          What the hell?

Mike laughs.

                    BOB
          What time is it, son?

                    SCOTTIE (climbing in bed with
                    Bob)
          What do you care?

Bob, dazed, is looking around himself, like he is being
had.

                    SCOTTIE (amusing Mike)
          Why, you wouldn't even look at a clock,
          unless hours were lines of coke, dials looked
          like the signs of gay bars, or time itself was a
          fair hustler in black leather... isn't that right,
          dude?

Bob staggers out of bed wretching and spitting. Then
back into his waking stupor, feeling something is being
put over on him.

> SCOTT
> There's no reason to know the time. We are
> timeless.

Bob checks his wallet.

> BOB
> Aren't you forgetting, Scottie my boy, [A
> GOVERNOR'S SON], that we who steal, do so at
> midnight?

Bob's money and cocaine are gone. Bob turns angry
and bellows.

> BOB
> What the...who ripped me off? Budd!!!
> Budd!!!!

*S*tairs again.

> BUDD
> Yes, Bob!!!

Budd stands at the stoop and comes through the door,
just as Bob is running out.

> BOB
> I fell asleep and have been robbed!

> BUDD
> Jane!!!

*T*he room below.

Jane Lightwork, the owner of the established hotel,
comes to arms. She is very old.

> JANE
> You'd think that I could keep the peace in my
> house...

Bedroom.

Scottie and Mike laugh. Mike gets down on his hands
and knees and tries to scoop up a little cocaine from
the floor.

Hall.

> JANE
> Bob, Bob we'll find your drugs. We'll find
> them.

Another hall.

Bob is storming down it in a rage, people opening doors
of the rooms.

> BOB
> Jane, I know you well enough...

Yet another hall.

Hotel dwellers are watching Jane move down the hall
answering Bob.

> JANE
> I know you, Bob... you owe me money, Bob,
> and now you pick a fight with me, and are
> disturbing the peace of my hotel.

MAIN derelict hall of the hotel.

Bob parades, in his night clothes, in front of a gathering of outcasts in the hotel.

> **BOB**
> This hotel is full of thieves...junkies!

> **JANE**
> You are the thief!

> **BOB**
> They picked my pocket!

LAUGHTER from the throngs of outcasts. Jane enters a balcony overlook of the main hall. Mike and Scott enter, arms around each other, laughing.

> **JANE**
> It's impossible to board a dozen or so men and women who live honestly and have the others live like junkies.

One of the dwellers listening to the argument is shooting up as they speak. We see a close view of the needle and Bob running around in the background.

Bob makes his way next to Scott.

> **BOB**
> You have corrupted me, Scottie, I was an innocent before I met you...and now look at me...just a little better than wicked. I used to be a virtuous man...

Scottie is laughing at him.

> **BOB**
> ...well, virtuous enough. I swore a little. I never gambled more than seven times a week. Poker. I never picked up a street boy more than once a quarter...

Scottie laughs.

> BOB
> ...of an hour. Bad company has corrupted
> me. I'll be darned if I haven't forgotten what
> the inside of a church looks like.

> MIKE
> Where do you find your strike tonight, Bob?

> SCOTTIE
> I see a good change for Bob to make. From
> Stealing to Preaching.

> BOB
> Stealing is my vocation, Scott. It's not a sin
> for a man to labor at his vocation.

> GARY
> Hey...psst...

The three gather around Gary.

> GARY
> Very early tomorrow morning, there will be
> small time rock and roll promoters coming
> back from their show. Every night, they walk
> home with the loot and they stop by the Grotto
> Bar, one mile away from here, and more often
> than not they've been drinking already. If we
> can't steal from them on their way to the bar,
> we can get them when they come out. See,
> dude?

> MIKE
> I'm not gonna rob anybody. I'd rather sell
> my ass. Straight and simple. It's less risky.

> BOB
> So long as I don't know these guys
> personally...it's okay with me.

> GARY
> They're from Beaverton. New to the
> business...

                    MIKE
Not me. I'm not going along on this crackpot
scheme. Especially since Gary thought it up.

                    BOB
Come off it, Mikey. Find a better way to
make a buck. Something to fall back on,
other than your ass.

                    MIKE
Scott's inheritance.

Bob walks away from the two others.

                    SCOTT
                 (whispering)
Come along, Mikey. I have a joke I wanna
play...a joke I can't pull off alone...

Mike laughs and joins Bob, hugging him around his fat
belly.

                    BOB
Oh, my sweetheart, come and rob with us
tomorrow.

                    MIKE
I was going to come anyway.

SCOTT hugs the others too.

                    MIKE
We'll be rich!!!

Scottie dances away.

                    SCOTT
Provide for us, oh great psychedelic Papa!

Scottie grabs Denise and kisses her then begins to leave
through the door. He throws her to Mike who catches
her and runs off with her.

                    Scottie
Good catch dude...and meet me on three
street!

                       37

Scott leaves, Bob follows him:

Outside the derelict hotel.

>   BOB
>   Scott. When you inherit your fortune, on
>   your twenty-first birthday, let's see...how far
>   away is this?

>   SCOTT
>   One week away, Bob, just one more week.

>   BOB
>   Let's not call ourselves robbers, but Diannah's
>   foresters. Gentlemen of the shade. Minions of
>   the Moon. Men of good government.

>   SCOTT
>   (under his breath)
>   When I turn twenty-one, I don't want any
>   more of this life. My mother and father will
>   be surprised at the incredible change. It will
>   impress them more when such a fuck up like
>   me turns good than if I had been a good son
>   all along. All the past years I will think of as
>   one big vacation. At least it wasn't as boring
>   as schoolwork. All my bad behavior I'm going
>   to throw away to pay my debt. I will change
>   when everybody expects it the least.

Scott turns and leaves.

>   BOB
>   And you will become a hard roller, a hatchet
>   man for your old man.

Scott laughs to himself, because he knows Bob is
misunderstanding him. Bob is part of the past life that
he says he is going to throw away.

>   SCOTT
>   No! You will be the hatchet man, Bob, that
>   will be your job, and so there will rarely be a
>   job hatcheted. It will be one big endless party,
>   won't it?

Bob laughs. Scott walks across a field.

                    BOB
          Well, at least my little friend has offered me a
          job. They are so good to me.

*I*nside the Broadway Cafe. Day.

Denise and Mike hang out together. Both are smoking
cigarettes which have made a billow of smoke that
hangs over the table that is in the front window.

                    DENISE
          Moms are great, because, you know, I could
          always go to my mom and say, hey I need a
          new lipstick, and she would always give me
          money for that. That was great.

                    MIKE
          I only saw my mom once, but I remember
          what she looked like. She was very beautiful.

                    DENISE
          What do you mean, once?

                    MIKE
          When I was born.

                    DENISE
          How could you remember when that god-awful
          thing happened?

                    MIKE
          Dunno. But I remember it. Yeah, I remember
          how beautiful and kind she was. She was
          good.

                    DENISE
          And she split from you, huh?

                    MIKE
          Maybe she didn't mean to.

                    DENISE
          Did you see what was going on, Mike? Between
          Pinky and Dale? Did you see that? That's the
          third fight I've seen today. Things always
          happen in threes.

                    MIKE
          I don't know. They have a sort of, ah,
          relationship. Between them.

Across the street there are three people, a TALL MAN,
who has his hat stuck on his boot and a lady and
another man with a dog on a leash.

                    MIKE
          I don't know about that, but, ah, listen, what
          you and me talk about, it's just between us,
          you understand? Hey, what's over there, see
          those assholes? Who are they, you know any
          of them?

                    DENISE
          I can't see that far.

DENISE STANDS AND OPENS THE FRONT DOOR AND YELLS
ACROSS THE STREET.

                    DENISE
          HEY!

The group across the street look up and begin yelling
back, but we cannot hear them.

*U*nder the Burnside Bridge, day.

Mike and Denise kiss, and their arms are entagled in a
loving, but awkward embrace. Twigs and leaves are
caught in Denise's hair as they are lying on the ground.

Different STILL COMPOSITIONS OF SEX while they are
lying in the wilds under the bridge.

                         40

Then...

Denise lights a cigarette.

> **DENISE**
> That reminds me, I gotta send my Ma a
> Christmas card, I still haven't done it yet.

> **MIKE**
> Yeah, I haven't done it either.

> **DENISE**
> Your mom lives in Idaho right now?

> **MIKE**
> Yeah.

> **DENISE**
> I used to live in Montana.

> **MIKE**
> My own cousin. He's dead. And my grandma,
> that's one...two...it usually comes in threes.

> **DENISE**
> Does come in threes.

> **MIKE**
> My cousin died, my grandmother died, and
> right after she died, her daughter died. My
> aunt. Within a year. And they wuz all
> women, not even a year, six...well....six
> months-eight months, three women in the
> family died.

A pause.

> **MIKE**
> That's funny, huh? I WONDER WHY YOU
> THOUGHT THAT, cuz, my FATHER says stuff like
> that.

> **DENISE**
> Well, my grandma was superstitious.

MIKE

My father told me that, said things usually
come in threes...and I said, aw....you're
crazy.

A Long pause. A motorcycle passes, someone yells, and
a horn honks.

MIKE

It sounds crazy. That's my lucky number too.

DENISE

Huh?

MIKE

Three.

DENISE

Mine's eight.

MIKE

I like three.

DENISE

You know why I like eight?

MIKE

Why?

DENISE

Cause of the eight ball. You know. When
you're stuck behind the eight ball? I fuckin'
feel stuck behind the eight ball today, I'll tell
you. The business is so slow in the middle of
the week, you know that Mike?

*P*ublic bathroom. Night.

Mike empties the contents of his pockets at a bathroom
sink. He has in his possession: One condom. One comb
with blond hair stuck in it. One nickel. Half a stick of
gum. One knife with the letter W stamped on it.

He arranges these things in a neat order on the surface of the sink while a man flushes a toilet in the background and uses another sink. Mike is quite at home here. He takes his time arranging the articles, and washing his hands. He looks over at the man washing his hands and gives him a friendly smile.

The man leaves. Mike puts all the things on the sink into his pockets. Then he walks over to a urinal, unzips his fly and starts to take a leak. A shadow opens the door in back of him, and without turning around, Mike senses the presence of a man.

*A*lleyway.   Night.

Scottie is helping Bob with a disguise, putting on pants over a large belly, with medallions around the neck.

> SCOTT
> How long has it been, Bob, since you could see your own feet?

> BOB
> About four years, Scottie. Four years of grief. It blows a man up like a balloon.

Mike and Budd appear, running, with costumes on. There are two others behind them.

> MIKE
> There's rock and roll money walking this way!

> BUDD
> And they're drunk as skunks.

> MIKE
> This is going to be easy. We can do it lying down.

> SCOTT
> But don't fall asleep, now, Mike.

43

                    BUDD
          Shh!! Here they come!

                    SCOTT
          You four should head them off there!

                    BOB
          We four? How many are walking with them?

                    MIKE
          About six.

                    BOB
          Huh, shouldn't they be robbing us?

Scottie laughs. Bob waddles along the side of the
alleyway, stepping on a curb, then in a pothole losing
his balance. Another accomplice whistles from atop a
building. We SEE the group of ROCK AND ROLL
promoters.

Bob walks further from Mike and Scottie.

                    SCOTTIE
          If they escape from you, we'll get them here.

Bob struggles as he walks.

                    BOB
          Eight feet of cobblestones is like 30 yards of flat
          road with me.

Mike and Scott run off, laughing at him.

                    BOB
          I can't see a damned thing in here.

                    BUDD
          Jesus, will you shut up! And keep on your
          toes!

Budd sees the promoters coming and waves to Bob as he
lies down on the ground.

                    BUDD
          Lie down!!

                      44

                    BOB
    Lie down!?

                    BUDD
    Lie down and stay quiet, until they round the
    corner and we'll ambush them.

                    BOB
    Have you got a crane to lift me up again?

Budd laughs.

                    MIKE
    They're coming!!

*D*own the way, the rock and roll promoters are
approaching, having no knowledge of the buffoonery at
the other end of the tunneling alleyway. They are
drunk.

                    VICTIM 1
    Come along neighbor, Tommy will lead the
    way. I've lost track of time...(burp)

*A*t the other end of the alley:

Bob and three others are marching in procession,
chanting, a facsimile of Rashneesh, but a bad act.

The rock promoters approach, smashing a bottle.

                    VICTIM 1
    Who are these jokers?

                    VICTIM 2
    Rashneesh, listen!

                    45

Scottie and Mike hide behind garbage cans, laughing.

The rock promoters circle the group of chanting
Rashneesh.

                              VICTIM 3
                   I thought that all you Rashneesh had up and
                   left...

Victim 1 pours a beer on one of their heads. Just as he
does this Bob pulls out two long pistols, almost heavy
enough that he cannot hold them straight, barrels
parallel.

                              BOB
                   Aha! One move and I'll blow you away, you
                   sully scumbags, up against that wall!

One of the victims falls down and begins to run away.
One of Bob's men starts after him. A lockbox that he
was carrying falls to the ground. Bob spies it.

                              BOB
                   No! Let him go!

Bob aims one pistol at the running figure as he keeps
the others against the wall with the other pistol. He
fires three times. One of Bob's boys grabs the lockbox.

A VIEW of the running figure, bullets cutting around
him.

                              BOB
                   Look at him go!

                              VICTIM 2
                   Don't shoot us!

Bob winks at the lockbox and shoots the gun in the air.

All the rock promoters go running. Bob charges after
them, firing the gun twice more in the air, then once
at the lockbox, breaking it open.

                                 46

                        BOB
         The valise is open. Let's see what we got.

Mike and Scottie hiding behind trashcans.

                      SCOTTIE
         Where are our disguises?

Mike runs to his stash and finds two large capes and
large hats. They put these on.

Bob finds wads of money and receipts.

                        BOB
         Ticket anyone? To next week's show?

He throws these on the ground and the boys fall over
themselves for the tickets. Bob wads the money and
puts it back in the box, laughing to himself.

Mike and Scottie sneak closer to the group still hiding,
long flowing capes concealing their identity.

                        BOB
         Scott and Mike have disappeared, did the shots
         scare them away?

They sneak closer. Mike lights a big firecracker and
waits.

                        BOB
         ...maybe we should get the hell out of here.
         But, are they such chickens?

A LOUD EXPLOSION!

Mike and Scottie, disguised, jump out with large silver
baseball bats, swinging them and making as much noise
as they can, knocking over a set of garbage cans,
flashing flashlights into Bob and the others' eyes.

Frightened, Bob drops the lockbox and runs, the others
follow, Mike and Scottie hitting them with the bats as
they go.

                         BOB
          Get the box! Oh, fuck!

Mike swings the bat at Bob, it grazes the side of a
building and sparks fly from it. Bob wheezes from the
run.

Scottie chases the others in the same direction.

They stand, kicking garbage cans and watching them
run, convulsing with laughter.

                      SCOTTIE
          The thieves scatter!

                       MIKE
          Bob Pigeon will sweat to death!

*J*ack Favor enters the Governor's CHAMBERS day.

                       JACK
          Can anyone tell me about my son?

He walks across the room.

                       JACK
          It's been a full three months since I last saw
          him. Where is my son Scott?

                        AID
          We don't know, sir.

                       JACK
          Ask around in Old Town, in some of the
          taverns there. Some say he frequently is seen
          down there drinking with street denizens.
          Some who they say even rob our citizens and
          store owners. I can't believe that such an
          effeminate boy supports such "friends."

A high overhead (helicopter?) view of the country landscape in the early morning. Far below us on a lonely road is a small dot, a motorcycle, traveling east.

*F*urther along on its travels, the motorcycle crosses a steel BRIDGE.

*O*ld Town day.

Scottie and Mike, riding on a stolen motorcycle, sweep through the early morning streets without being noticed.

*S*topping at a stop light in the city.

Scott pauses to think.

>   SCOTT
>   Mikey, do you realize how long I have been
>   here out on the streets, on this crusade?
>
>   MIKE
>   About as long as the rest of us. I mean. I
>   can't even remember that far back, Scott, I
>   mean......
>
>   SCOTT
>   It's been three years, Mike.
>
>   MIKE
>   Wow...that's a really long time, Scott. Have I
>   been here three years, too?
>
>   SCOTT
>   What I'm getting at, Mike, is that we are
>   survivors.

                    MIKE
Yeah, well, so, isn't that obvious?

                    SCOTT
Yes. It is incredibly obvious. They could drop
a bomb on this city and you know what we
would do?

                    MIKE
    (thinking)
DIE?

                    SCOTT
No. We would survive. Because we are _____.

                    MIKE
Survivors!

                    SCOTT
Right, Mike.

                    MIKE
Say, Scott. Whaddya say we go survive over
at the Broadway Cafe a little bit, at least it's
warm over there.

*I*nt. Broadway Cafe. Day.

Mike and Scott sit around the table with Carl and Mary.
Mike blows a smoke ring.

Denise runs in the door of the cafe, excited about
something.

                    DENISE
MIKE! Scottie! There's a man from City Hall
down the street. He wants to speak with you,
Scottie.

                    SCOTT
What's that?

                    DENISE
He says that he's sent by your father.

                      50

                    SCOTT
Say hello and send him to my mother.

                    MIKE
What kind of a man is it?

                    DENISE
A young man. And he's got cops with him.

                    SCOTT
Cops....

*S*treet exterior day.

Two POLICEMEN and one OFFICIAL are walking down the
street toward the Broadway cafe.

*B*roadway Cafe interior day.

The cops enter, passing The PROPRIETOR of the cafe, an
aging heavyset woman named NANCY.

                    NANCY
Good morning, officers...

                    COP 2
How are you this morning, NANCY? Don't
mind if we take a look around your place, do
you?

One officer is already inspecting the stolen motorcycle
outside.

Mike sees this, and looks the other way from the cop
who is peering in the Broadway cafe window.

                    COP 1
Have you seen the young Scott Favor?

                        51

                              NANCY
            I do believe he was here just a second ago.

Nancy looks in the front window.

                              NANCY
                Oh, yeah, there he is.

Nancy points Scott out.

Scott is giving Denise a long kiss, hiding from the cops.

The OFFICIAL walks to the front window of the Cafe.

Scott pretends he is being rudely interrupted.

                              SCOTT
            Ah-ha...what have we here?

                              OFFICIAL
            Excuse me...Mr. Favor...we have been sent in
            search of a fat man...a large bearded....

                              COP 3
            ...FAT MAN...

                              COP 2
            Goes by Bob Pigeon.

                              SCOTT
            Bob Pigeon?

                              COP 1
            That's right.

                              SCOTT
            What do you want with him?

                              COP 2
            Ahem. There's been a report, sir, he has been
            involved in a holdup...

                              COP 1
            Last night. Have you seen him?

                    SCOTT
I saw him around last night, when was the
holdup?

                    COP 1
Late. Two in the morning.

                    SCOTT
I saw him about four, but he wasn't very loose
with his wallet. Did he get away with any of
the money?

                    COP 2
Yes, indeed, sir...two thousand dollars of a
rock promoter's money.

                    SCOTT
Well, anyway, I haven't seen him _recently_.
Why do you look here?

                    COP 1
They say he has friends here.

                    SCOTTIE
I beg your pardon.

                    COP 2
Sorry...

                    OFFICIAL
Sorry for the interruption. We have a
message for you from your father. He says
that he would like to see you as soon as
possible.

THE OFFICIAL HANDS SCOTT AN ENVELOPE.

                    SCOTT
Thank you for your message.

Scott takes the envelope and puts it on the table.

Street, day.

The police close the door.

>   COP 1
> Hmmm.

>   COP 2
> What about the dead body.

>   COP 1
> Let's not get Favor's kid involved in this report
> if we can help it. But if he were my son,
> I'd....

Cop 1 makes a fist and slams it in the palm of his other
hand.

INT. Broadway Cafe.

>   MIKE
> Bob is a wanted man now.

>   SCOTTIE
> And as dangerous to be around as cops
> themselves.

>   MIKE
> We need a hiding place.

>   SCOTTIE
> Where should we go?

>   MIKE
> To visit my brother.

>   SCOTT
> You have a brother?

>   MIKE
> Yes, I have one.

                    SCOTT
        Where is he?

                    MIKE
        He's in........he's in.......

Mike suddenly begins to shake, and, falls asleep.

Scottie picks up the envelope from his father and puts
it in his pocket.

Mike and Scott are stuck on a long straight road in
the desert. Mike is angry at Scott because he doesn't
think he knows how the motorcycle works.

Scott is trying again and again to start the engine.

> MIKE
> Come on...

> SCOTT
> Shut up, Mike.

He tries to turn it over again.

> SCOTT
> If I had known that it was going to be this
> hard to start, then I wouldn't have stopped it
> at all.

Mike looks at the road and the surrounding area. It is
the same road that he was stuck on in the beginning.

> MIKE
> Scott? I just know that I have been on this
> road before.

Mike stares at the face in the road. Two cactus for
eyes, mountains for hair, a cloud shadow forms the
mouth over a red nose road with a dotted line running
down it.

At night, Scott and Mike sit next to a fire they have made on the side of the road. We can hear Indians in the distance dancing and chanting a song.

> MIKE
>
> It sure is lonely out in the desert.

> SCOTT
>
> Yeah, I guess.

> MIKE
>
> If I had had a normal family, and a good upbringing, then I would have been a well adjusted person. But somehow that just didn't work out.

> SCOTT
>
> Depends on what you'd call "normal."

> MIKE
>
> Well, normal, you know, with a mom and a dad and a dog and shit like that...normal.

> SCOTT
>
> So you didn't have a dog? Or you didn't have a dad...

> MIKE
>
> I didn't have a dog and I didn't have a dad. Well, not a normal dad...

The music is getting louder. It sounds like a war chant.

> MIKE
>
> Hey Scott?

> SCOTT
>
> What?

Mike is hesitating. He is about to say something personal. He looks at Scott and back to the fire, a few times too many.

                        SCOTT
        What, Mike?

                        MIKE
        Oh. Have you ever.   Uh...

Scott is getting Mike's drift.

Mike rubs his crotch.

                        MIKE
        I mean, don't you ever get horny?

                        SCOTT
        Yeah.   But...

                        MIKE
        Oh, yeah...not for a guy.

                        SCOTT
        Mike. Two guys can't love each other. They
        can only be friends.

An awkward moment passes where Mike is looking away
from Scott and Scott can't help but look at Mike. Then
Scott catches Mike's eye and motions for him to come
closer to him.

Mike walks over to Scott and Scott holds him in his
arms.

Overhead VIEW of the two in front of the campfire.

                        SCOTT
        I only have sex for money...

Mike starts to get out some money.

                        SCOTT
        I can't take your money.

A pause.

                        SCOTT
        But we can be close friends.

The next morning. Mike is sleeping. As he opens his eyes, he can see Scott still trying to start the motorcycle.

Mike stands and looks down the road at an approaching State Police Car. Mike, afraid of the police, starts to move into the bushes.

Scott is out of breath trying to start the bike.

                    MIKE
          Scott, look...

Scott looks in the direction of the police car.

                    SCOTT
          Looks like this is it.

                    MIKE
          Yeah.

Scott hits the side of the gas tank of the bike with the palm of his hand.

                    SCOTT
          Can't get the bike started. Cops are coming.
          Stuck in the middle of nowhere with a stolen
          bike. Yeah, Mike. Looks like this is the end.

The policeman pulls up to them and parks.

The policeman sits in his car for a second and reports into the radio, then he gets out and walks over to the boys.

Mike gets scared and runs into the desert.

The cop stands and watches. Mike has nowhere to go, he is running into an open desert.

The policeman, a full blooded American Indian, seems amused at his power. He looks at Scott then back at Mike, who trips in the desert and falls in a cloud of dust.

                    COP
          What's the matter with him?

                    SCOTT
          I don't know. I guess he doesn't like cops.

                    COP
          Yeah.

                    SCOTT
          That's how it looks.

                    COP
          What are you kids doing out here?

                    SCOTT
          This cycle is one bitch to turn over. But you
          probably don't know about motorcycles. You
          aren't a motorcycle cop.

                    COP
          I turned a few.

Scott walks through the desert looking for Mike where he dropped. He picks him up out of the dirt, spit dripping from his sleeping lips, and smacks him in the face.

                    SCOTT
          Wake up, Mikey, the heat's off.

Mike will not wake up.

*W*hen Mike wakes up. He is inside a TRAILER at night.

Scott is eating sandwiches to his right that are on a little T.V. tray.

There is MIKE's BROTHER leaning into him on his left. He looks at Mike offensively. His brother is very good looking, but looks like he has lost his mind somewhere down the line. Which is why he lives in the desert in a trailer, away from people.

> SCOTT
> Look, Mike. Sandwiches.

> BROTHER
> Your mother...now she was a right woman. She used to be so proud of you...you know...she would just beam. And not Jim Beam either. If you know what I mean. We used to drive for hours to get a look at you. I remember, what was it...eighteen years ago?

> MIKE
> Twenty-one.

> BROTHER
> Is that how old you are now? I thought you wuz younger than that...what? Well anyway, we would start off in the morning to see you, and it would take an hour to get to the institution. You were maybe one year old. What? I wasn't proud that you had to live in an institution, mind you...but all the same, when I would look at you, all the institutional walls would come down and we were a family. Your mom, me, and you. God knows where dad was.

Mike is getting visibly upset. Scott gets up to go to the bathroom.

Inside the bathroom night.

Scott enters and notices a velvet portrait of a woman hanging on the wall. Off screen Scott can hear Mike and his Brother.

> MIKE (o.s.)
> I don't belong to you, DUDE...I'm not yours...

> BROTHER (o.s.)
> (his voice booms out so unexpectedly deep
> and loud that Scott is startled)
> <u>Shut your mouth</u>! Don't you talk back...

His brother hits the table with a crash.

Living room night.

> BROTHER
> Well...(takes a breath)
> Anyway. You were maybe not in the
> biological sense, my brother, but in our
> business, bro... (holds his hands up in the air)
> And if I'm not your brother, how's come you
> turned out exactly like me then?

Mike has gotten the jitters and fallen asleep in front of him.

Scott enters from the bathroom.

> BROTHER
> Oh, he'll come out of it. It's like this
> whenever we get together. It's always like
> this when we get together. It's the way that
> we say hello to each other.

He holds his head down.

                    BROTHER
    I'm all that he's got. But he doesn't want me.
    He doesn't care. He'd rather live out on the
    streets. I love him, though.

Scott looks around the trailer at all the velvet portraits
hanging on the walls.

                    BROTHER
    Oh. I paint these for a living. But sometimes
    the people don't send the check when they get
    finished. So I keep them. I like them.

Ext. Trailer. Night.

Mike and his brother sip iced tea. Colored lights
decorate the trailer.

                    BROTHER
    Want me to tell you what happened to your
    Mom? Have you ever heard it? Did you ever
    hear what the hell happened to her?

                    MIKE
    No. But I don't care.

                    BROTHER
    You loved her, and don't tell me you didn't. I
    know you did.

                    MIKE
    I didn't even know her.

                    BROTHER
    Yeah, you loved her, though.

                    MIKE
    I already heard what happened to her.

                    BROTHER
    But you don't know the whole story. One
    thing about the truth. It's interesting.

                    MIKE
    I don't care.

BROTHER

If you had known her, you would care. She
would see guys on the side. At night. When I
wouldn't be around...maybe I'd be in San
Francisco or some darned place, doing my own
business. God knows where. She would see
guys...yeah....anyway.....along comes this
guy. A guy we both knew. A guy who was
into cards. A gamblin' man. And he said
that he used to herd cattle in Argentina. I
dunno, maybe he did, and he had a bit of
money. More'n I had at that point in time.
But it was funny, the way he gambled. He
was not safe in the friends that he made. So
his money would come and go real fast....

MIKE

I never heard this one before.

BROTHER

So this guy, your Mom fell for. What? She
went cuckoo over this guy. Well, their affair
went on for a year or so and your mom
wanted to marry this guy. She was already
married to our real dad. So he said no. He
didn't love her anyways. But she wanted him
to marry her. And to have a little family.
That's when you were born. As a matter of
fact, you were really the cause of this whole
mess. She wanted to make a little family and
take you and this guy someplace and set
something up.
    (slaps his leg with his hand)
A family thing! Ridiculous, right. A card
man. Had a bunch of money, but could have
just as well lost it on his next hand. Probably
did too. Well you'll see what I'm getting at.

MIKE

That's not how I heard it.

BROTHER

Yeah, I know. You heard it from me and I'm
telling it different this time, see? So this Mom
of yours found herself a fuckin' gun. I

BROTHER (continued)
thought she was going to blow me away with it
one night. She got so into this gun. She
would flash it to anybody that gave her
trouble. She would sleep with it. Yeah...
strange, huh? She would stir fry vegetables
with the loaded gun. What? I mean......
What? I used to say, politely, "Mom, don't go
stirring up dinner with the gun, now, you'll
blow a hole in the frying pan." What?

Mike begins to cry.

BROTHER
And she used to do other things with this gun.
Sexy things with it. Oh, boy, she was into
this thing. I just thought it was some sort of
weird phase that she was going through. And
so anyway, this guy, who she was cuckoo
over, brought her to the movies one night. A
drive-in movie in a stolen car, don't-cha-
know, what? And the movie was....ah....RIO
BRAVO or some shit like that. And well, she
went and shot this guy....don't-cha-know.

MIKE
You're making this up as you go along, bro.

BROTHER
And they didn't find him until the next show,
RIO BRAVO playing on the big screen. Spilled
popcorn soaking up the blood.

Mike begins to really cry now, bawling and coughing.

SCOTT
(who has been listening)
Oh, come on, how corny, man....

BROTHER
No. Your mom had to split, and split she did.
And that guy. That guy was your real father.

65

                         MIKE (sniffs)
          I knew that was coming. You sure do like to
          make me cry, bro.

                         BROTHER
          And I got this card from her, not too awful
          long ago. Maybe a year.

Mike's Brother hands him a postcard with a Holiday Inn
motel on the front of it. Written on the card, Mike's
mom says she is working as a waitress there, in the
"Blue Room" of the Holiday Inn off Interstate 85 outside
Boise, Idaho. He also hands him a *picture* of his mom.

Mike and Scott wore sunglasses as they journeyed
onward to the Blue Room, Scott driving the motorcycle
and Mike riding on the back.

Night time exterior of the Holiday Inn.

Mike and Scott pull up on the motorcycle and park it.

Inside the Holiday Inn.

A hostess is standing in front of a sign that bills
"Shecky Crude" as the featured entertainer of the
evening in the "Blue Room."

Mike is speaking to the hostess. He shows her his
picture of mom.

                         MIKE
          My mother works here. Her name is Dorothy.

                         HOSTESS
                    (thinks for a second)
          No. I can't think of anyone by that name.
          Let me get the manager.

                              66

The hostess picks up the phone.

Manager's office night.

A MANAGER is sitting behind his desk wearing a shiny
blue suit, he shifts in his swiveling chair, and looks at
the Holiday Inn Postcard that Mike's mother sent to his
father.

> MANAGER
> Dorothy, Dorothy.....There was a Dorothy
> Biondi used to work here a year ago, but she
> split. Saved up all her money and headed to
> Italy.

> MIKE
> To Italy?

> MANAGER
> Yeah. It took her forever to save any cash,
> but she did, and flew away. She was looking
> for her family. I guess she came from Italy.
> But she didn't look Italian.

> SCOTT
> Was your mom Italian?

> MIKE
> I don't know. I guess that she was.

In the lobby of the Holiday Inn at night.

Mike and Scott witness the arrival of the German
Mercedes Benz parts salesman.

> SCOTT
> There's that guy.

> MIKE
> Who?

                    SCOTT
         The guy who gave us a ride from Portland.
         What's he doing here?

Scott and Mike walk up to him. HANS turns and a
broad smile crosses his face.

                    HANS
         Mike! Scottie! How good to run into you! My
         dear boys! How have you been?

Inside Hans' hotel bathroom. Night.

Mike lies in a bathtub in sudsy water. There is a
pounding on the bathroom door.

                    MIKE
         I just got in the tub! Wait your turn.

                    HANS
         But Mike! Don't you want anything to eat? We
         are ordering room service. Ya?

                    MIKE
         Ahhh.   Room service?   Ya!   Let me see.
         Two hamburgers, with cheese, onions, lettuce,
         tomato, no pickles. A Coke and french fries.

                    HANS
         O.K. That's hamburger wiz everything, no
         pickles, Coke, french fries.

                    MIKE
         That is correct.

                    HANS
         Thank you.

                    MIKE
         You're welcome.

As Mike and Scott eat their hamburgers, Hans sits across from them next to a small desk light on a double bed in his Holiday Inn room.

                    HANS
          How are the hamburgers, boys?

                    MIKE
          They're okay, Hans.

                    SCOTT
          Good, Hans. I don't think that I've tasted a
          hamburger as fine as this Holiday Inn
          hamburger.

                    HANS
          I'm glad that you like it.

The boys eat approvingly.

                    HANS
          How did you boys get so far? I only left you in
          Portland a few days ago.

                    SCOTT
          We rode on our trusty motorcycle.

                    HANS
          And what brings you to the Holiday Inn?

                    SCOTT
          Business.

                    HANS
          What kind of business?

                    SCOTT
          We're selling motorcycles.

Still images of Mike, Scott and Hans having sex in the motel.

Hans rides his newly purchased motorcycle across the plains from Boise to Picabu, Idaho. A local policeman pulls him over doing 95 mph in a 45 mph zone.

At the Boise Airport Scott and Mike stand in a ticket line. The ticket taker stamps their tickets.

> TICKET TAKER
> Do you have any baggage?

Mike and Scott shake their heads no.

I t a l i a

Mike wakes up and finds himself sitting beside the Trevi fountain in Rome. There are other street kids surrounding him fishing for coins that tourists have thrown in the fountain. He doesn't see Scott.

He looks around a bit.

                    SCOTT (o.s.)
          Mikey! Over here!

Mike's VIEW of Scott in a taxi cab.

The TAXI pulls up to a small farmhouse on a hill outside of Rome. Mike and Scott get out and walk around the house. A farmer is cutting his crop on the next hillside.

A DOG walks up to them.

The taxi driver gets out of the car and asks for his money in Italian. Scott holds out the money that he has and the driver takes it, counting it out for himself.

Mike walks around a corner of the house and notices the doors are open as the cab drives off down the drive.

Scott sits down on the stoop in front of a shack and Mike steps into the house.

                              MIKE
          Mom? .... Hello?

An extremely *Beautiful Italian girl* walks around the
corner where Scott is sitting. He can't see her. And
she leans against the shack and stares at him, then
looks up at Mike, who is walking through the house
trying to find someone.

                              GIRL
          Hello.

Scott looks up at her, a little surprised.

                              SCOTT
          Hi. Is this your house?

The girl is a little shy and leans on the shack.

                              GIRL
          No. This isn't my house, but. It is my
          uncle's house.

                              SCOTT
          I'm Scott.

                              GIRL
          I'm Carmella.

                              SCOTT
          And he is Mike. We came from America to
          find his mother.

                              CARMELLA
          Oh. An American woman?

                              SCOTT
          Yeah, do you know her?

                              CARMELLA
          Yes, but. It is not true that she lives here.

                              SCOTT
          It isn't true?

                               72

CARMELLA

No. She left a long time ago. Back to
America.

SCOTT

Oh, shit. Was she your friend?

CARMELLA

I wanted to speak English, and she taught it to
me.

Mike walks from the house to Scott and Carmella.

CARMELLA

Hello. My name is Carmella.

MIKE

I'm Mike.

CARMELLA

Hello Mike.

SCOTT

She knows your mom.

Later in the afternoon, Mike is inside of a room in the
house, and he is crying. He is talking to Scottie, who is
holding him.

MIKE

I mean, Christ, we come all this fuckin' way
and she ain't here either. Where'd she go
from here?

Mike walks through the rooms of the Italian country
house.

MIKE'S VIEW of a room, and Scott is just closing the
door. He winks at Mike as he shuts it.

Inside the room, Carmella and Scott lay down on the bed and kiss.

Scott takes off his clothes and ravishes Carmella, tearing at her dress.

Carmella is naked and the two grab and twist with each other on the white bed.

Still views of the lovemaking.

Mike in the country, watching the farmer in the field.

Mike approaches the house and there is a taxi cab waiting. Carmella is putting a suitcase in the trunk.

Scott helps Carmella in the front seat of the taxi.

                    SCOTT
          Hey, Mike. Let me talk with you for a second.

Scott follows Mike inside the house and into a room.

                    SCOTT
          I'm gonna take some time off.

Scott gives Mike an American Express card.

                    SCOTT
          Don't leave home without it. Ha-ha.
               (Mike doesn't think it's funny)
          I mean, maybe I'll run into you down the
          road.

Mike is shocked but sees what Scott needs to do as he looks out the window and can see Carmella in the taxi.

> MIKE
> Yeah, sure. Okay.

> SCOTT
> Sorry about this, dude.

> MIKE
> I'll be okay. Don't worry about me.

> SCOTT
> Sorry, but....

> MIKE
> No, man, forget it. Hurry up, she's waiting, you're gonna lose her.

Mike hides a tear.

> SCOTT
> All right. You sure you'll be okay?

> MIKE
> Go on, get out of here.

Outside, a dog watches the taxi leave down a rutted dirt drive.

> MIKE'S THOUGHTS:
> Well. So much for the great protector-of-us-all. Protector of himself, more like. I couldn't believe Scott would leave me here in the middle of a foreign country.

Inside, Mike goes into one of his fits, snorting, a little like a pig, and falls asleep.

P o R t l a n d

*M*ike wakes up in an airline's passenger seat. A
STEWARDESS is leaning over him.

> STEWARDESS
> Wake up. Wake up, we're here.

> MIKE
> Where? Where am I?

> STEWARDESS
> You're in Portland.

Int. BROADWAY CAFE in the day.

Mike sits at the round table in front of the window.

Denise is with a new boy, STUART, and are making
out. Mary sits and chain smokes cigarettes, there are
three other UNKNOWNS around the table.

> MIKE
> And so, I was back in Portland, enjoying the
> life I used to lead. It was like I was back from
> a vacation. Denise had a boyfriend now....

E_{xt.} street night.

Cars cruise by. Mike is on a street corner. He hops into a stranger's car.

I_{nt.} MOTEL night.

Still views of Mike having sex with a date.

> MIKE
> ...and I enjoyed the fruits of my labor.

CLOSE VIEW of money exchanging hands.

B_{ROADWAY} CAFE day.

Mike is at the table again, smoking a cigarette.

There are three new kids who look very MEAN, and are hassling another kid, pulling his collar and throwing him around.

> MIKE'S THOUGHTS
> And there were new kids who were coming
> around who wanted to take your money. It
> was a dark period for the streets. Normally,
> Scott would keep order in the Broadway Cafe.

A Hot Dog stand. Gary cheerfully prepares Mike a hot dog.

> MIKE'S THOUGHTS
> Gary and Ray both got work at stands.
> It was funny...

I̲nt. Deli day.

Ray serves Mike a hot dog.

> MIKE'S THOUGHTS
> ...they both sold hot dogs. Which is what
> they were used to selling on the streets in the
> old days. These guys had really changed, I
> thought.

M̲ike's FACE, outdoors in the daytime.

He looks out on the cityscape.

The buildings of the city uproot and tumble in the air.

J̲akes restaurant night.

Mike wakes up. He is sitting next to Bob and Budd. A
new friend, a colorfully dressed man named BAD
GEORGE, who looks like a street minstrel, talks on the
street in front of a fancy restaurant. Bad George is
obnoxiously yelling in Bob's face.

> BAD GEORGE
> Bob! What tidings I bring you. And such joy.
> Some of that old rot gut that you and I used
> to drink. I have three bottles stashed in the
> bushes out on eighty-second.

> BOB
> What blew you in?

> BAD GEORGE
> Think of the fun we can have, if we could only
> find a ride for a journey to the bushes where
> the hooch is hid.

                              BOB
If I shared your wine, I might catch this awful
disease you appear to have. My clothes would
turn striped, and I would suddenly have bells
on my toes, like this here...

Bob points to George's bells on his shoes.

                          BAD GEORGE
Bob, you're one of the greatest living men on
Three-street.

                              BOB
That is correct.

                          BAD GEORGE
Surely you can find us a ride somewhere.

                        MIKE'S THOUGHTS:
As I listened to Bad George and Bob talk, I
watched across the street as a long black car
pulled up alongside one of the fancier
restaurant/bar establishments of Portland.
And who got out of that car? It was the old
protector-of-us-all, himself.......Scottie
Favor.

Bob notices the group of men getting out of a car in
front of the restaurant. One of them is <u>Scottie</u> , in a
three pieced suit. He is with his Italian girlfriend.

                              BOB
If it isn't Scottie Favor himself. Blessed are
they who have been my close friends. Now
dressed in a three pieced suit and looking
every bit a gentleman! He has run into his
inheritance.

                          BAD GEORGE
Who?

                              BOB
George, Budd, Mike. We have waited for this
day to come.

Bob charges in the direction of Scottie and his friends.

Int. Jakes. Night.

Scottie and his associates, who are men much older
than he, perhaps in their thirties, make their way
through the yuppie crowd standing in the bar drinking.
Hellos and how-do-you-do's are directed at Scottie. A
man stops Scott on his way through the crowd.

>   MAN
>   Scottie! I haven't seen you in a dog's age.
>   You're looking well. So grown up. Scottie, I'd
>   like you to meet Ed Warren, he's in marketing
>   at Nike. Ed, this is Scottie Favor.

>   ED
>   Oh, Jack Favor's son, hello, pleased to meet
>   you.

>   SCOTTIE
>   How do you do?

Bob is following Scottie through the crowd. Scottie
walks past Hans, who is having a drink with another
man. They recognize each other but neither speak.

Bob, with Bad George in tow, straightens himself up as
the yuppie crowd looks on disapprovingly. Their smelly
clothing betrays them.

>   BOB
>   Come, George, watch this. You will see the
>   attention that I get.

Bob looks at his clothes. A bouncer spots them.

>   BOB
>   It's true we're drawing attention to ourselves.
>   But Scottie will see that I am dying to see
>   him, and it won't matter how we're dressed.

Scotty and his friends are sitting around a crowded table. As they take their seats, Scottie hears Bob bellowing.

VIEW of Bob being detained by the bouncer.

> BOB
> God save you! God save you, my sweet boy.

Scotty turns away from Bob, so his back is to him.

> BOB
> Sonny! My true friend!

Silence for a second, the crowd grows quieter.

> BOB
> I mean you, Sonny! It's me, Bob!

Without turning toward Bob, Scottie speaks.

> SCOTT
> I don't know you, old man.

> GIRL IN CROWD
> Who is that bum?

Scottie turns and meets Bob, who kneels next to him.

> SCOTTIE
> Please leave me alone.

Bob is thinking that Scottie's attitude is a joke.

> SCOTTIE
> Don't think that I'm the same Scottie that I
> was before. Everyone has noticed that I have
> turned away from that life, and the people
> who kept me company.

Bob is shocked.

Outside, Mike can see through the windows of the restaurant, Bob and Scottie talking.

Int. Jakes. night.

> SCOTTIE
> When I was young, and you were my street tutor. An instigator for my bad behavior, I was trying to change. Now that I have, and until I change back.....don't come near me.

Bob feels the rejection like a shock. Stares at Scott for a second, then he's pulled away by the bouncer.

Ext. Jakes. night.

Mike watches Bob and Budd sit down with him.

> BUDD
> Don't take all this seriously. It's one of his jokes.

Nighttime overhead view of Bob in his greasy derelict hotel bed. He is having nightmares, and suddenly he *CRIES OUT!*

> BOB
> God, God....God!

Dawn views of the city.

*M*ike awakes atop a downtown building.

Inside the Derelict Hotel Day.

Mike enters, and walks through a very quiet, although crowded MAIN ENTRANCE. There is a body on a slab in the middle of the room that is covered with a sheet.

                    MIKE
          Pigeon?

                    A BOY
          Scottie Favor broke his heart.

                    GARY
          He's gone now, either to Heaven or to Hell.

                    JANE LIGHTWORK
          Be sure it isn't to Hell. He tried to be an
          honest sort. I'm the one who heard him cry
          out last night. He said God, God, God... three
          or four times. And when I got there I put my
          hand into the bed and felt his feet. And they
          were cold as stone. And I checked the rest of
          his body. And it too was as cold as stone.

                    BUDD (crying)
          It sure is quiet.

Mike approaches Budd.

                    MIKE
          I guess you're gonna miss him the most, Budd.

Mike gives him Scottie's American Express card, as others carry his body out of the hotel.

                    MIKE
          Here. Maybe you can give him a good burial.

Budd cries.

Mike exits.

In the country, Mike looks at the road.

He has visions of sagebrush and rock flying into the air as if picked up by a big wind.

Then he lies asleep by the side of the road.

> MIKE'S VOICE
> I suppose that a lot of kids like me think that they have no home, that home is a place where you have a mom and a dad.

Pause.

> MIKE'S THOUGHTS
> But home can be any place that you want. Or wherever you can find.....My home is right here on the side of this road, that I been to before. I just know I been on this fucking road one time before, you know that?

Later, a car drives by Mike's sleeping body by the side of the road. It turns around and stops next to Mike. A figure puts Mike in his car and drives off down the road.

> MIKE'S THOUGHTS
> Sometimes I had thought that God had not smiled on me, and had given me a bum deal. And other times, I had thought that God had smiled on me. Like now. He was smiling on me...for the time being....

Int. Car. Day.

Scott is driving the car. He looks over at Mike sleeping.

Ext. Desert. Day.

The car disappears down the road.